PLANT BAS
COOKBOU
BEGINNERS

and

MEDITERRANEAN DIET COOKBOOK FOR BEGINNERS

2 in 1 Bundle

G.S. Van Leeuwen

Disclaimer

The information contained in " PLANT BASED DIET COOKBOOK FOR BEGINNERSandMEDITERRANEAN DIET COOKBOOK FOR BEGINNERS" is meant to serve as a comprehensive collection of strategies that the author of this eBook has done research about. Summaries, strategies, tips and tricks are only recommendation by the author, and reading this eBook will not guarantee that one's results will exactly mirror the author's results. The author of the eBook has made all reasonable effort to provide current and accurate information for the readers of the eBook. The author and it's associates will not be held liable for any unintentional error or omissions that may be found. The material in the eBook may include information by third parties. Third party materials comprise of opinions expressed by their owners. As such, the author of the eBook does not assume responsibility or liability for any third party material or opinions. Whether because of the progression of the internet, or the unforeseen changes in company policy and editorial submission guidelines, what is stated as fact at the time of this writing may become outdated or inapplicable later.

Sommario

CHAPTER THREE 86

Plant-based diet dessert recipes **86**

CHAPTER FOUR 121

CHAPTER FIVE   156

CHAPTER SIX   174

CHAPTER SEVEN 186

CHAPTER EIGHT 211

CHAPTER EIGHT   317

CHAPTER NINE   352

CHAPTER TEN   372

CHAPTER ELEVEN 395

CONCLUSION 409

PLANT BASED DIET COOKBOOK FOR BEGINNERS

THE ULTIMATE LOW-CARB COOKBOOK TO SAFEGUARD YOUR DIET with Quick, Easy, Delicious, and Perfect Fast & Easy Recipes for Busy People

G.S. Van Leeuwen

INTRODUCTION

A plant-based diet is a diet focused on plant-based foods. It involves meat substitutes such as fruit, vegetables, cereals, legumes, legumes, nuts and soy products.

Individuals often have different interpretations of how they feel like a "vegetable-based" diet. Many people still have small amounts of animal products like meat and fish, but mostly focus on vegetarian cooking. The Pescara diet is a strategy that includes fish during meat cutting. People who eat dairy products and eggs without consuming meat and fish are considered vegetarians and those who cut animal products including dairy products, milk, honey and jelly are called vegans.

People who follow plant-based diets and consume a wide variety of fruits, vegetables and pulses are likely to find it easier to achieve their target of five days. As a result, they are also likely to have good intakes of fiber and the vitamins and minerals found in fruit and vegetables, including folate, vitamin C and potassium, all of which are important for good health.

It should be noted, however, that' plant-based' does not mean' good' automatically, especially when it comes to processed and packaged food. Technically, foods such as refined sugar, white flour and certain vegetable fats can all be considered' plant-based' as they are vegetarian, but this does not mean that they should make up the bulk of a healthy diet.

CHAPTER ONE
What Is a Plant-Based Diet

A plant-based diet emphasizes the consumption of anything derived from plants - vegetables, cereals, nuts and seeds - minimizing or excluding animal products. While some may think that a plant-based diet is just another term for a vegetarian or even a vegan diet, there is a fundamental difference. Plant-based diets emphasize the consumption of whole and natural foods and avoid processed foods such as tofu, seitan or packaged products, even if they are technically vegan or vegetarian.

Plant diet is a term that comes from the English plant-based diet, which would have to be translated as a plant-based diet. It evokes obvious associations with veganism, but do these terms really mean the same thing?

Veganism is often understood as a whole lifestyle that includes the fight to reduce animal suffering, pro-animal activism, and attitudes associated with it. A plant-based diet is, in this respect, a much narrower concept, limited only to diet. There are a few minor differences. A plant-based diet does not have to be 100% plant-based. May allow small amounts of meat, fish, or dairy products. However, veganism does not allow this possibility. On the other hand, the plant-based diet should be health-oriented and based on low-processed products, while veganism is not necessarily the case. Many vegans like to eat unhealthy products if they were prepared without the participation of animal components.

To sum up - the plant diet assumes that most calories come from plant products that are low-processed and composed in the diet so as to promote good health and may or may not be a vegan diet.

Plant-Based Vs. Vegan & Vegetarian

In some major ways, vegetable-based diets are different from vegan or vegetarian diets. First, let me explain the distinction between vegans and vegetarians: Lacto-Ovo vegetarians consume dairy and eggs, while vegans avoid all animal products and generally avoid the purchase, use, and use of animal products. Vegans and vegetarians that eat foods that are refined packaged, and may not even end up eating a healthy diet.

People on an herbal diet, on the other hand, eat whole foods as close to nature as possible: vegetables, fruits, nuts, seeds, and the like. Someone who follows a plant-based diet can choose to eat vegan or vegetarian and may or may not use animal products. Some people who follow a generally plant-based diet can consume some products of animal origin, but they include a very small portion of their diet.

1. Eat fully on plant foods

Eating real food that grows from earth is the most important thing. Most likely, the reason people don't eat enough plant-based food is that they still don't realize how strong plant nutrients are in maintaining our health.

Most people still feed on the flesh and products of other animals, not because there is something so natural, necessary or rational about it, but primarily because the major marketing share in supermarkets, stores, and food advertising are occupied by meat, animal, fast, processed and packaged products. Vegetable foods without salt, sugar, and refined fat still account for only a small percentage of the food industry's profits.

At the same time, it is the complete plant foods that are proven to have the most healing effect on our bodies. Cardiovascular disease, diabetes, obesity, osteoporosis, asthma, gout, and any chronic illness have an indisputable link to nutrition, lifestyle, and physical activity. And that's good news. All we need to do is be empowered enough to choose the right foods and live actively.

Vegetable food is at the heart of any healthy diet. Plants are the natural repositories of chemical elements assembled under one sheath in their most complete and complete form. They contain all the vitamins, minerals, antioxidants, isoflavones, essential fatty amino acids, and all other yet-to-be-tested phytonutrients that can sustain the life and health of all of us. Every breakthrough in medicine, any medicine that is used to suppress the symptoms of an illness as a result of an unhealthy lifestyle, contains active ingredients derived from a plant or chemical element synthesized on the basis of one already existing in a plant.

Therefore, eating plants is the first and most important condition for living in health and well-being. Everyone has a very intimate, emotional, and even addictive relationship with the food they eat. Therefore, the task of vegans is not only to teach compassion for animals and the care for nature that is irreversibly destroyed by industrial animal husbandry but also to break the dependence of most people on aggressively advertised animal and processed products. People's true connection to food is that of plant food.

2. Plant foods to be whole

Eating only plant food is not enough to stay healthy. Everyone is a complete organism made up of whole cells. That is why all of our cells need the most comprehensive food we can provide.

Whole plant foods mainly include fruits, vegetables, grains, and legumes in their least processed and natural state. Nuts and seeds are also part of an entirely plant-based diet, as are mushrooms (though not plants), spices, and all green leaves. Eating whole foods restricts or excludes processed and extracted substances such as extracted fats, sugars, and proteins. This means as much as possible without extracted oils, no added sugar, and artificial sweeteners, no superfood packets of powders, or protein shakes.

Eating whole foods does not mean catching and eating an entire onion without cutting it, nor eating as a raw eater. The idea here is not to deprive the ground food of its essential components, such as fiber, phytonutrients, antioxidants, etc. Removing fiber from fruits and vegetables, for example, raises blood sugar levels, and the consumption of extracted fats causes the blood plasma to become greasy, and the arteries clog. Of course, this also means eliminating packaged foods whose content label is a whole lesson in chemistry.

Whole-grain flours, edible milk or fermented foods as tempe are not technically whole foods since in the process of processing some of their substances are lost, but from a health point of view, they are much closer to whole foods than bottle fat, protein isolates or sweeteners such as glucose-fructose syrup. Many foods can be vegan, but at the same time, they are excessively concentrated sources of salt, sugar, and fat. So when we talk about eating whole foods, we do not mean absolutely excluding everything that is not food in its entirety but to adjust in the most convenient way for us to base from vegetable sources of carbohydrates, fats, and proteins in there at least a processed form.

3. Carbohydrates should be at the base

In addition to the need for whole foods, our cells need, above all, sufficient energy. The main source of energy in the human body is food, which, when eaten, is broken down into its main nutrients - carbohydrates, fats, proteins, and water. Of these, it is the carbohydrates that make the cells draw on their glycogen supply, the fuel that makes our body's engine run at full speed.

All whole plant foods contain a full supply of these macronutrients. There are no plants that contain any of them. However, the difference is in their percentage in each food. Fats and proteins are also extremely important for our physical and mental health. However, in order to have a balanced diet, carbohydrates must be the highest percentage of the substances we take with our food.

The basis of good nutrition in healthy people with normal physical activity is that about 80% of the total calories a day comes from carbohydrates, 10% fat, and 10% protein. This is the best ratio of foods with which the body can completely metabolize glucose. This diet is the most natural thing for a man. The world's healthiest nations, including the Bulgarian people, have historically eaten the largest number of carbohydrate-based plant foods. Potatoes, corn, different varieties of wheat, millet, rice, buckwheat, all kinds of fruits and vegetables.

Popular low-carb diets for weight loss may indeed have a quick effect, but with prolonged exercise, they pose serious health risks. The problem with blocked blood vessels does not exist only with meat and animal products. Even coconut oil, oil, and olive oil can cause blood to become greasy and blockage of the artery walls with a plaque of fat.

Fat accumulation prevents glucose metabolism, so if you eat carbohydrates from whole grains, fruits, and vegetables, but continue to gain weight, then the problem is not the carbohydrates, but the fat accumulated in your blood vessels from before. So if someone is going for carbohydrate plant foods, I recommend first doing at least one week of healing cleansing to clear the fat and plaque accumulated before starting eating the right foods in the required amounts. Before we get to the right food, it is a good idea to create the necessary prerequisites for its absorption and for our body to get used to the new regime.

4. Don't drink your calories

Drinking them is one of the easiest ways to burn excess calories in your body.

We now know that a statistically significant number of people may be drinking between 800 and 1200 calories a day from morning coffee or distemper, from coca-cola, energy drinks, or cappuccino to work, from the beer with friends afterward, or a glass of wine before going to bed. The problem is, our brains don't even register those calories as calories. Like any other creature on the planet, one does not need to drink anything but water to be healthy. If you still want to drink coffee, drink it clean - no added sugar. If you make herbal tea, drink it without any additional sweetener. In just a few days, you will notice how much more saturated and fresh you will feel.

It is known that digestion begins in the mouth when we are salivating. The more food is chewed, the better it is metabolized. I'm also a fan of juices, especially carrots, but it's a good idea not to discard the garbage fibers, but at least put some in the cup of juice.

If you stop eating your calories, you will immediately feel how much more energy you will have throughout the day. Most of these drinks contain large amounts of sugar and other sweeteners that instantly raise blood sugar, followed by an equally dramatic drop. This insulin reaction becomes even more dangerous when we add to the fact that we drink these fast carbohydrates without fiber and ballast in minutes and even seconds.

This means that we will have a quick burst of energy within minutes of drinking the sweetened beverage, but that will come back to us like a boomerang, and we will head down in the early afternoon. On the other hand, when we eat slow carbohydrates from whole foods, they contain a large amount of fiber, which regulates the smooth distribution of blood sugar and the flow of energy to our cells, so that we are constantly alert and fit.

5. Move

Proper nutrition is not the whole story when it comes to human health. Just as we need a balance between nutrients for the body to function most optimally, so do we need a balance between diet, movement, and other lifestyle-related factors.

In addition to the storage of nutrients in whole plant foods and herbs, exercise also plays a preventative role in protecting us from cardiovascular disease, hypertension, diabetes, obesity, osteoporosis, protecting us from colds, infections, and depression. Physical activity improves functions of blood circulation, lungs, skin and muscle tone, healing of wounds, and lowering of bad cholesterol.

If you improve your diet, physical activity becomes a must. Without physical exertion, most people on a particular diet regain their weight loss or revert to their old lifestyle. Restricting calories or eating only once a day causes the body to store calories in the form of fat instead of burning them. The body prepares for an emergency of calorie deficiency, so it saves most of it as a supply. Therefore, a lifestyle that involves an abundance of whole foods high in slow carbohydrate foods that is physical activity-oriented and movement is much more likely to bring fat burning, good figure, and health in the long run.

In the first 10 minutes of moderate physical activity, the body burns carbohydrates, which are stored as glycogen in the muscles. With continuous movement and physical activity, the body begins to rely less and less on glucose and burns fatter. Trained muscles develop a much better ability to burn fat than untrained, and the more muscle you have in proportion to your body fat percentage, the more efficiently the food is metabolized to its nutrients. The more one body is trained,

The time to recover and rest after physical activity is the period when muscles are built. The type of exercise determines the size and shape of the muscles. For example, if you ride a bicycle, you will have more developed muscles in your legs and thighs, while, for example, one tennis player may have a much more developed leading arm than the other. However, as you can guess, the type of food also plays a very important role in building the physique.

A slow carbohydrate diet is most effective as carbohydrates from whole plant foods are the main and best source of glycogen for our cells. Physical activity dramatically increases the flow of oxygen, so foods rich in antioxidant vitamins A, C, and E are extremely important in the process.

In general, vitamins and minerals play a key role in releasing energy and restoring the body. Red beets and all green leaves are very valuable helpers in building red blood cells that transport oxygen to the muscles. Raw fruits, vegetables, seeds, and nuts are extremely important for building connective tissue and joints that are stressed in all kinds of physical exercises.

1. Improve Your Health Status

Over the past 5 years, scientific articles that show the benefits of increasing the consumption of plant-based foods have not ceased to be published, articles that indicate that following a more plant-based diet helps prevent and even reverse some of the diseases that they cause more incidences of deaths in the western world, being in many situations more effective than medication or surgical interventions.

This type of plant-based diet is the only one that has been shown to reverse the number 1 cause of deaths - heart attacks. Doctors such as Dean Ornish and Caldwell Esselstyn proved with their studies that they follow a low-saturated vegetable diet, rich in complex carbohydrates and basically vegetable-based protein, and changing some lifestyle habits (moving the body at least 30 min/day) cardiovascular diseases can be reversed.

A vegetable-based diet also helps prevent certain types of cancer, reduces the incidence of heart disease and diabetes, cholesterolemia, hypertension, Alzheimer's, Parkinson's disease, rheumatoid arthritis, ulcers, and vaginal infections.

A plant-centered diet has a positive effect on the prevention of accumulation of abdominal fat, the appearance of acne, aging, allergies, asthma, body odor, cellulite, eczema, metabolic syndrome, and body weight control.

With just increasing the consumption of fruits and vegetables, we increase the chances of extending our life expectancy, but a life with a higher quality of health. On the contrary, the consumption of meat and other foods of animal origin, such as dairy products, have shown that possibly due to its high content of saturated fats, arachidonic acid, and Hemo iron, life is shortened.

The consumption of meat, fish, dairy, and eggs also increases exposure to antibiotics, mercury, and other heavy metals and xenoestrogens in fish and carcinogenic substances in meat that are formed when cooked at high temperatures.

Contrary to popular belief, most vegans get enough protein in their diet, consume more nutrients than the average of omnivores, and usually maintain an adequate weight. There are only two vitamins that we cannot find in plant foods, these are vitamin D, which we get from sun exposure, and vitamin B12, produced by micro bacteria that live on earth, and from which one should be supplemented.

2. Maintain Your Proper Weight

The evil of many is the accumulation of weight that one adds up over the years, from the age of 22, the only thing that can grow is a belly or a tumor. So to prevent the birth of both follows, a vegetable diet will be our ally.

The reality is that if we consume many vegetables in our dishes, the caloric intake of these will decrease since, on average, a cup of vegetables gives us between 10-50 kcal. And if above, we are replacing with these ingredients other fatty, sweet, and processed foods, you will undoubtedly be reducing the calories consumed at the end of the day, and you will even feel fuller since you will consume more fiber.

3. Eat Healthy And Economical

Many people believe that eating healthy or plant-based foods is expensive, and they turn to processed food or junk, "fast food" because they believe it is the most economical. Certainly, this is not reality.

Visiting a fast-food restaurant such as Burger King and/or Mc Donalds to buy hamburgers, fries, and sodas will not be cheaper than buying 1 package of lentils, 1 package of rice, 1 onion and a bag of frozen spinach with what you can prepare a delicious and complete stew for the whole family.

The only thing you save by consuming these junk food restaurants is time, cooking time. But believe me that once you get into the kitchen, you can prepare twice as many servings, freeze them, and you have them for other days of the week. It's just about being practical and sometimes a little creative, playing with different spices, seasonal vegetables, and different cereal or legumes.

Lentils, beans, and peas are some of the most economical and high nutritional value foods you can find in the supermarket. When we talk about fruits and vegetables, we should always go for the options that are in season, and even buy extra when they are on sale and freeze them for when it is not their time. So I do with blueberries and other fruits of the forest, to have a proper reserve of local production in winter.

Amazing Benefits Of A Vegetable-Based Diet

1. Supports the digestive system

To prevent gastrointestinal problems such as irregular bowel movements, maintaining a healthy digestive system is necessary. Dietitians recommend adding dietary fiber into your diet to avoid indigestion-related adverse effects. In this context, a herbal diet seems appropriate as it contains choices filled with dietary fiber. In the morning, you should consider eating a bowl of freshly cooked whole grain cereals and in the evening serving salad made with organic vegetables to keep your digestion on track.

2. For cardiovascular health

Finding cardiovascular issues can be stressful, and long-term-and may lead to other debilitating complications of health, such as hypertension. This is where the reduction of red meat is important. Health experts agree that in this case, switching to a plant-based diet can help maintain a healthy cardiovascular, since plants contain a minimum of dietary cholesterol and saturated fats.

3. Promotes Weight Loss

Losing extra pounds seems impossible at times. Spending hours at the gym will not provide the desired result without making dietary changes. With a vegetable-based diet that includes vegetables, beans, grains, and legumes, you can get amazing results in a short time.

4. Safe for diabetics

Without thinking twice, people with diabetes should opt for a plant-based diet. Not only are nutrients like dietary fiber kept full for hours, but they also inhibit a rise in appetite. Diabetics can monitor their diet in this way-avoiding high production of insulin.

5. Promotes skin health

Red meat, processed foods, sweets from chocolate, and sugary drinks have adverse effects on your body. If you want to get flawless skin, eliminate these food options, introduce salads and smoothies made with organic fruits and vegetables.

6. Keeps your body energetic

An active body contributes to increase the quality of your life. Staying in a constant state of tiredness or sleep can affect your daily performance. You should address the issue through dietary changes such as opting for a vegetable-based diet.

7. Promotes psychological health

A stable state of mind is nothing short of a blessing. Many studies have shown that the nutrients found in whole grains, green leaves, and citrus fruits have positive psychological health effects. These sources, not to mention, are a vital part of a plant-based diet.

8. Lowers High Cholesterol Levels

According to cardiologists, plague and accumulation in the arteries contribute to cardiac arrest. You should consume lower or no fat and cholesterol-lowering food options to maintain LDL levels in your body. That's where beans, grains, and fruits come into play. Just go to them and make a difference.

9. Fight Insomnia

A herbal diet ensures uninterrupted sleep for 8-9 hours. It can disrupt your sleep cycle by eating processed and fatty foods or snacks before bed because food takes a long time to digest, and you can wake up exhausted and groggy the next morning. The consequence of this time of restlessness is an insomnia-a deteriorating sleep disorder. Take a bowl of vegetables at least two hours before bed and see the impressive results.

10. For high blood pressure

The adverse effects of high blood pressure should not be ignored. Nutritionists suggest that at 45, which is alarming, about 55% of adults are highly susceptible to high blood pressure. To some degree, you can eliminate the risk by following a herbal diet because it does not contain any side effects that are often present in red meat.

11. Increases Metabolic Rate

Stimulated metabolism facilitates your overall well-being. This helps you lose weight as well. Despite this, the metabolic rate decreases after reaching adulthood. The best way to increase your metabolism is to eat foods like lentils, beans, green leaves, and citrus fruits.

12. Fighting Cancer Cells

Many plants contain compounds that are sufficiently active to prevent cancer cells. You can not spread cancer to other parts of your body in this way. Nonetheless, further research on the effectiveness of a plant-based diet in patients with cancer is ongoing.

13. Promotes Longevity

Due to the nutrients found in herbal food sources, it is possible to live a long and healthy life. Through facilitating the functioning of each organ, these components reinforce the body. Most of these sources of food are rich in vitamin C, which rejuvenates damaged cells and tissues that fight premature aging symptoms.

Foods to Eat on a Plant-Based Diet

From eggs and bacon for breakfast and steak for dinner, animal products are the focus of most meals for many people.

When switching to a vegetable-based diet, meals should focus on herbal foods.

If animal foods are eaten, they should be eaten in smaller quantities, paying attention to the quality of the item.

Foods such as dairy, eggs, poultry, meat, and seafood should be used more as a complement to a vegetable-based meal, not as the main focal point.

A-List of Herbal and Whole Food Based Shopping

- Fruits: Berries, citrus fruits, pears, peaches, pineapple, banana, etc.

- Vegetables: kale, spinach, tomatoes, broccoli, cauliflower, carrots, asparagus, peppers, etc.
- Starchy Vegetables: Potato, Sweet Potato, Pumpkin, etc.
- Whole Grains: Brown rice, flaked oats, farro, quinoa, brown rice pasta, barley, etc.
- Healthy fats: Avocados, olive oil, coconut oil, unsweetened coconut, etc.
- Vegetables: peas, chickpeas, lentils, peanuts, black beans, etc.
- Walnut seeds, walnuts, and butter: Almonds, cashews, macadamia nuts, pumpkin seeds, sunflower seeds, natural peanut butter, tahini, etc.
- Unsweetened herbal milk: Coconut milk, almond milk, cashew milk, etc.
- Spices, herbs, and condiments: basil, rosemary, saffron, curry, black pepper, salt, etc.
- Condiments: parsley, mustard, nutritional yeast, soy sauce, vinegar, lemon juice, etc.
- Herbal protein: Tofu, tempeh, herbal protein sources, or powders without added sugar or artificial ingredients.
- Drinks: coffee, tea, sparkling water, etc.

If you supplement your plant-based diet with animal products, choose quality products from supermarkets or, better yet, purchase them from local farms.

- Eggs: Raised to pasture when possible.
- Birds: Outdoor hunting, organic when possible.
- Beef and Pork: Grazed or fed on grass when possible.
- Seafood: caught from sustainable fishing when possible.
- Dairy: Organic dairy products from grazing animals, wherever possible.

A healthy diet based on plants should be focused on plant foods such as fruits, fruit, whole grains, legumes, nuts, and seeds. These should be eaten in smaller quantities relative to plant foods if animal products are consumed.

Foods to avoid or minimize

A plant-based diet is a way of eating that focuses on consuming food in its most natural form. This means that highly processed foods are excluded.

When buying groceries, focus on fresh foods, and when buying foods with a label, point to items with as few ingredients as possible.

Foods to Avoid

- Fast food: French fries, cheeseburgers, hot dogs, chicken nuggets, etc.
- Added sugars and sweets: table sugar, soda, juice, candies, cookies, candies, sweet tea, sugary cereals, etc.
- Refined grains: white rice, white pasta, bagels, white bread, etc.
- Packaged foods: cookies, crackers, cereal bars, frozen dinners, etc.
- Foods processed by vegan foods: Vegetable-based meats like Tofurkey, fake cheeses, vegan butter, etc.
- Artificial sweeteners: saccharin, sucralose, aspartame, etc.
- Processed animal products: Bacon, cold meat, sausage, beef jerky, etc.

Foods to minimize

While healthy pet foods may be included in a plant-based diet, the following products should be minimized in all plant-based diets.

- Beef
- Pork
- Sheep

- Game meat
- Poultry
- eggs
- Dairy Products
- Seafood

When following a plant-based diet, highly processed foods should be avoided, and animal products minimized.

Herbal diet for detoxification and weight loss

Research has shown the tremendous impact that cellulose can have on a diet. The recommended daily dose is at least 30 years.

Cellulose is a strong, thick, and flexible fiber that gives the fruits and vegetables structural integrity. It is the main part of the plant cell - up to 70% of the plant mass consists of cellulose, which contains more than half the amount of carbon in the biosphere.

It belongs to the fiber group, which also includes pectin, lignin, gelatin, and mucous membranes.

The daily portion in a plant-based diet should be 1,000-150 kcal for women and 1,500 kcal for men, in combination with at least 30 g of cellulose.

The main foods that can be consumed are lentils, baked potatoes, beans, corn, pasta, and bread made from standard flour. Salad vegetables, as well as any fresh and dried fruits - also.

It is good to rely on low- calorie and pulp-rich vegetables. Such are tomatoes, lettuce, cauliflower, asparagus, broccoli, cucumbers, and peppers.

Other foods rich in cellulose, such as cornflakes, nuts, and dried fruits, should also be included in the menu. They supply the body with 200 kcal and 15 g of cellulose.

myths about the plant-based diet

MYTH: VEGANS DO NOT GET ENOUGH PROTEIN

While we all tend to focus on consuming enough food, the fact is that this nutrient is not consumed too much by many Americans. Protein requirements can be met by an adequate vegan diet that includes vegetable proteins from sources such as nuts, beans, soy foods, quinoa, and seeds such as pumpkin seed. According to a recent study, even athletes with specific protein requirements will meet their quota by choosing a variety of vegetable protein sources.

One more thing: it is not necessary, as you have heard, to combine different vegetable proteins during meals (for example, by having beans and rice or peanut butter on a whole-wheat toast).

FACT: VEGANS NEVER EAT MEAT, FISH, DAIRY PRODUCTS OR EGGS

Strict vegans only eat plant food. While you may find vegetarians who consume dairy and eggs, people who follow a vegan diet do not eat animal by-products, including honey. Whether for animal welfare concerns, environmental reasons, health reasons, or weight loss or welfare beliefs, strict vegans only place food and plant-made products on their plates.

MYTH: BECOME A VEGAN ALWAYS LEADS TO WEIGHT LOSS

While you may lose weight in a vegan plan, it is not a guarantee. Although a review of the different diet patterns found that vegan diets can cause weight loss, you still need to eat well. After all, Oreos and French fries are free of animals, but they won't help you lose weight.

That said, if your diet consists mainly of fruits, vegetables, whole grains, and beans, you will get a lot of fiber, and a one-year study found that this change in the diet helped people lose approximately.

FACT: YOU NEED TO SUPPLEMENT A VEGAN DIET

Vitamin B12, which is essential for the cell division and maintenance of nerve cells, is the major concern for vegetarians. This nutrient is found only in animal products, not in plant foods, so if you don't eat animal foods like salmon, tuna, chicken, and beef, you may be short. The answer is an enriched cereal if you don't want to break a vitamin B12 pill (or a triple that would do the trick). Do not assume, though, that all cereals are fortified. For example, Cheerios does not contain vitamin B12, so you should read the labels to ensure that they are safe.

Vegans run the risk of falling short of other nutrients, such as calcium, iron, and omega-3 fatty acids, so it is a good idea to meet with a registered dietitian who can suggest how to meet your food needs or recommend a vegan supplement. quality.

MYTH: MEAT ALTERNATIVES ARE HEALTHIER THAN MEAT

It's not that easy here. Most meat imitators have a high sodium content that can increase blood pressure. The American Heart Association recommends that sodium intake be limited to the ideal, not exceeding 1500 mg daily. Some vegetarian burgers have 600 mg of sodium per hamburger in your grocery store's freezer aisle.

No matter what food camp you are in, the choice of whole foods instead of hyper-processed foods is nutritional advice that applies. Focus on staple foods without animal food, such as beans, nuts, whole grains, and fruits and vegetables, and you will be preparing for a nutritious vegan diet.

One last word about these packaged meat imposters: Don't think that all meat imitators are vegan. Morningstar Farms Bacon Strips lists egg whites as the first ingredient, so if you are a strict vegetarian, you will need to read the fine print.

CHAPTER TWO
Plant-Based Breakfast Recipes

1. Frankenstein Avocado Toast

Traditionally, Halloween festivities begin with the sunset, but mashing some avocado for this monstrous, fun, and easy breakfast will definitely elevate your mood. Best of all, the combination of complex carbohydrates and healthy fats will supply you with the fuel needed for a spooky day of costume contests, clothing, and decorations at work or school!

What you will need

- 4 slices of whole wheat bread
- 1 avocado, cut in half and seeded
- 1 tablespoon lemon juice
- ½ teaspoon garlic powder
- A pinch of sea salt

DECORATIVE INGREDIENTS

- 1 nori leaf or a dark lettuce leaf
- Black beans
- Sliced red pepper
- Mexicrema dressing

Process

- bread in a toaster or in a toaster oven.
- While the bread is toasted, place the avocado in a bowl.
- Add the lemon juice, garlic powder and salt, and pestle with a fork or potato masher.
- Trim the nori leaf or dark lettuce to form the hair.
- Decorate the Franken toast forming the hair with the nori or the lettuce, the eyes with the black beans, the mouth with the sliced pepper, and the frame of the face with the dressing.

2. The quick and easy bowl of oatmeal for breakfast

What you will need

- ½ cup of quick oatmeal
- ½ - ⅔ cup of hot or cold water
- ½ cup of vegetable milk
- 1 teaspoon of maqui berry powder or acai powder (optional)
- ½ cup of fresh grapes or berries
- banana (or a whole banana, if you prefer)
- Walnuts
- Seeds

Process

- Combine oatmeal and water in a bowl, and let them soak for a few minutes.
- Cut the banana and grapes or berries as you wish, and add them to the oatmeal.
- Pour vegetable milk over oatmeal and fruits.
- Cover with nuts, seeds, powdered maqui berry or acai powder. I use walnuts and hemp seeds.

3. Almond butter toast with sweet potatoes and blueberries

What you will need

- 1 sweet potato, sliced half a centimeter thick
- ¼ cup almond butter
- ½ cup blueberries

Process

- Preheat the oven to 350-360 ° F (177 ° C).
- Place the sweet potato slices on baking paper. Bake until soft, approximately 20 minutes
- Serve hot, coat with peanut butter and cranberries. Store any leftover sweet potato slices, without dressings, in an airtight container inside the refrigerator for a week. Reheat them in a toaster or in a toaster oven and cover them as instructed.

4. Tropical smoothie in a bowl

Smoothie bowls provide texture and substance, which makes smoothies feel more like a good breakfast.

What you will need

- 2 cups frozen mango pieces
- ½ cup frozen pineapple chunks
- 1 frozen banana
- ½ to 1 cup of vegetable milk
- 2 tablespoons chopped nuts of your choice
- ¼ cup chopped fruit of your choice

ADDITIONAL ADERTS

- 1 tablespoon flaxseed flour
- 1½ tablespoons coconut pieces

Process

- Add the mango, pineapple, banana and vegetable milk (1 cup creates a thinner shake, and ½ cup makes it thicker) in a blender and mix everything until you get a smooth mixture.
- Put the smoothie into a bowl and cover it with nuts and fruit.

5. Oatmeal Seasoned with Vegetables

This tasty twist of traditional oatmeal contains a variety of vegetables and turmeric to start the day with a healthy breakfast.

What you will need

- 4 cups of water
- 2 cups of "cut" oatmeal (quick-cooking steel-cut oats)
- 1 teaspoon Italian spices
- ½ teaspoon Herbamare or sea salt
- 1 teaspoon garlic powder
- 1 teaspoon onion powder
- ½ cup nutritional yeast
- ¼ teaspoon turmeric powder
- 1½ cup kale or tender spinach
- ½ cup sliced mushrooms
- ¼ cup grated carrots
- ½ cup small chopped peppers

Process

- Boil the water in a saucepan.
- Add the oatmeal and spices and lower the temperature.
- Cook over low heat without lid for 5 to 7 minutes.

- Add the vegetables.
- Cover and set aside for 2 minutes.
- Serve immediately.

6. Pumpkin and Spice Oatmeal

What you will need

- 2 cups of vegetable milk
- 1 teaspoon pumpkin pie spice
- 4 seedless dates
- 2 tablespoons of raisins
- 2 cups pumpkin puree
- 2 cups of flaked oatmeal

Process

- Mix the milk, dates, raisins, and spices in a blender.
- Combine the milk mixture with the pumpkin puree and oatmeal in a medium container.
- If the mixture is very thick, add a little more milk.
- Cover and refrigerate for at least an hour or ideally overnight.
- Enjoy the heat or the cold.

These delicious pancakes are fluffy and popular with adults and children! Everyone keeps coming back for more. The combination of almond milk and rice vinegar creates the buttery taste that people crave.

What you will need

- 3 cups oatmeal
- ½ cup of millet flour
- ½ cup ground flax seeds
- 1 teaspoon of sea salt
- 1½ teaspoon baking soda
- 2 teaspoons baking powder
- 4 cups vanilla almond milk
- 2 tablespoons rice vinegar
- 1 tablespoon maple honey or date paste
- 1 tablespoon pure vanilla extract
- 3 tablespoons unsweetened applesauce

Process

- Mix the dry ingredients in a bowl.
- In a different bowl, mix the liquid ingredients.
- Pour the liquid ingredients over the dry ones and combine them well.

- Process the mixture well in a blender until smooth and lump-free.
- Heat a pan over medium-low heat.
- Using a ladle, pour the desired amount of mixture into the pan.
- Turn the pancake when bubbles appear on the top, and underneath it is firm for approximately 5 minutes.

8. Showy avocado toast

What you will need

- 2 slices of bread
- 1 avocado, sliced
- ½ lemon juice
- 2 tablespoons pumpkin seeds
- 1 pinch red pepper flakes
- 1 pinch smoked paprika
- 1 pinch of sesame seeds
- 1 pinch of salt
- 1 pinch of black pepper

Process

- Toast the bread.
- Place the avocado slices on the toast.

- Sprinkle the lemon juice over the avocado.
- Sprinkle pumpkin seeds, red pepper flakes, sesame seeds, salt and black pepper on top, to taste.

9. Millet and buckwheat muffins with black currants

What you will need

- ½ cup (90 g) of millet
- ½ cup (80 g) of unroasted buckwheat groats
- 4 chopped figs
- ¾ cup (160 ml) oatmeal or rice milk
- 1 tablespoon applesauce
- 1 heaped tablespoon (40 g) peanut butter
- 1 large ripe banana
- 1 pinch of sea salt
- 2 heaped teaspoons of baking powder
- ¾ cup (100 g) blackcurrants, fresh or frozen

Process

- Dip millet and buckwheat overnight (or all day) in separate containers. Wash and drain (a filter can be used).

- Soak the chopped figs in ¾ cup (160 ml) of oat milk for at least 30 minutes.
- Heat the oven to 300-350 ° F (177 ° C).
- Put the ingredients, except baking powder and blackcurrants, in a blender and mix them until a homogeneous lump is formed without lumps. Do not worry; It is supposed to be quite liquid since millet inflates considerably.
- Now mix the baking powder. Unplug the blender and finally combine (DON'T LIQUID) the currants with a spoon.
- Divide the dough into 9 muffin pans and bake for 33 to 35 minutes, until golden brown.

10.Apple and pumpkin pie

What you will need

- 1 spoon ground flax seeds + 2 ½ tablespoons water (flax egg)
- ½ cup all-purpose gluten-free flour (or oatmeal)
- 1 ½ cup quick-cooking oatmeal
- 1 tablespoon baking powder
- 1 teaspoon baking soda
- 2 tablespoons pumpkin pie spice
- 1 tablespoon cinnamon

- 4 medium granny smith apples
- ½ cup date pasta
- 1 cup pumpkin puree
- 1 teaspoon vanilla extract
- ¼ cup of water (optional)

Process

- Preheat the oven to 350 degrees F.
- Mix ground flaxseed (flax) seeds with water in a small bowl and set aside for 10 minutes.
- Mix all dry ingredients in a large bowl.
- Cut the apples into thin slices and place them in a container.
- Add the pumpkin puree, vanilla extract, flaxseed with water, and date paste to apples and mix well.
- merge the dry ingredients with the apples and mix well. Add water if the mixture seems to be too dry.
- Place the mixture in an 8 x 11 (2 quarts) container suitable for baking and bake for 30-35 minutes.

11.Pumpkin and oatmeal bars

What you will need

- 3 cups thick oatmeal
- 1 cup seedless dates
- ½ cup of boiling water
- 2 teaspoons pumpkin pie spice
- 1 tablespoon ground flaxseed or chia seeds
- ¼ cup small sliced nuts (optional)
- ¼ cup of vegetable milk
- 1 cup mashed pumpkin

Process

- Preheat the oven to 350 degrees Fahrenheit.
- Cut the date into small pieces, put them in a bowl, and pour hot water. Rest for 10 minutes.
- Add dry ingredients to the bowl and mix well.
- Add dates to the dry ingredients along with water, pumpkins, and plant milk and mix well.
- Cover the square bread with baking paper and push the mixture firmly into the bread.
- Cook for 15-20 minutes.
- Allow the mixture to cool completely in the container, then cut into 16 squares or 8 large bars.
- Store in the refrigerator for up to 7 days.

12. Beginnings with sweet potato

This is a great way to use leftover yams or sweet potatoes you've baked a day before or two. A delicious, sweet, and substantial start to your day!

What you will need

- 2 yams or baked sweet potatoes
- 2 peeled and sliced bananas
- 1 apple, without the heart and chopped
- ½ teaspoon ground cinnamon

Process

- Peel and cut the yams or baked sweet potatoes.
- Combine with bananas and apples.
- Mix the cinnamon.
- Briefly heat in a microwave oven. Serve hot.

13. Oatmeal breakfast muffins

These compact and moist muffins are like eating oatmeal coated with bananas and raisins in a bowl, and only these can be eaten directly with your hands!

What you will need

- 2½ cups of flaked oatmeal
- ½ cup oatmeal

- 1 teaspoon baking powder
- ½ teaspoon baking soda
- ½ teaspoon salt
- 1 tablespoon cinnamon
- ½ teaspoon ground nutmeg
- 4 ripe bananas, crushed
- 1 grated apple
- ½ cup non-dairy milk
- 2 teaspoons vanilla extract
- ½ cup raisins
- ½ cup chopped walnuts (optional)

Process

- Preheat the oven to 300-350 ° F (177 ° C).
- In a large bowl, combine and beat the dry ingredients.
- In a small bowl, combine bananas, apple, non-dairy milk, vanilla, and stir until well combined.
- mix the wet ingredients to the dry ones and combine them well. Add raisins and nuts, if you use them.
- If you use a mold for 6 muffins, bake for 45 minutes. If you use a mold of 12 muffins bake for 35 minutes.

14.Blackberry and lemon muffins for tea

What you will need

- 2 cups whole grain wheat flour for baking
- ½ cup of Sucanat (refined cane sugar)
- 1½ teaspoon baking powder
- 1 teaspoon grated lemon peel
- ½ cup natural soy yogurt
- 1 cup non-dairy milk
- 1 tablespoon lemon juice
- 2 egg substitutes (2 tablespoons ground flaxseed with 6 tablespoons water)
- 1 cup blackberries
- 2 tablespoons coconut with reduced-fat and sugar-free content (optional)

Process

- Preheat to 350 ° F (177 ° C) in the oven.
- Fill a paper-coated mold for 12 muffins (or use a non-stick skillet).
- In a medium bowl, mix flour, sucanat sweetener, baking powder, and rubbed lemon peel.
- In a separate bowl, mix soy yogurt, milk, lemon juice, and egg substitutes.
- Pour into the dry mixture the wet mixture and stir until it is hot.
- Carefully add blackberries.

- In the prepared muffin pan, distribute the mixture evenly.
- Sprinkle the coconut (optional) on top of the muffins.
- Bake them for 45 minutes in the preheated oven or until one of them has a toothpick inserted in the middle. Until serving, let them cool slightly.

15. Cherry and poppy seed muffins

What you will need

DRY

- 1 cup (120 g) raw buckwheat flour
- 1 ¼ cup oatmeal (155 g) oatmeal
- 2 tablespoons poppy seeds
- 2 teaspoons cinnamon
- ½ teaspoon cardamom
- 2 teaspoons baking powder

Wet

- 10 chopped figs
- A little more than 1 cup (260 ml) of vegetable milk, without sugar
- 2 ripe bananas

- 2 heaped tablespoons unsweetened applesauce
- 2 tablespoons peanut butter
- 1 pinch of sea salt (optional)
- ½ cup (50 g) dark chocolate (at least 70% cocoa), chopped
- 24 fresh or frozen cherries

Process

- Preheat the oven to 180 ° C (355 ° F).
- Cut the figs and soak them in vegetable milk for at least 30 minutes. If you want to dip it further, put it in the refrigerator.
- While the figs are soaked, chop the chocolate and place it aside. Put all other dry ingredients in a bowl. Put the figs and milk into the mixer. Add all remaining wet ingredients and mix until smooth.
- Pour the wet mixture over the dry ingredients and mix well. Make sure there are no lumps. Add chopped chocolate.
- The mold is filled with 12 muffins (molded using silicon) with a lump and finally hits two cherries in each muffin.
- Bake for 25-30 minutes. Allow it to cool a little before trying to remove it from the mold.

16. Cocoa, banana, and whole-grain spelled flour muffins

What you will need

- 2 large bananas (I use frozen bananas and then defrost them)
- 2 cups whole grain spelled flour
- 1 cup walnuts, chopped into large pieces
- ½ cup raw cocoa powder
- ¼ cup applesauce
- 1 cup almond milk
- ¼ cup maple syrup, 100% pure
- ½ teaspoon baking powder

Process

- Preheat the oven to 300-350 ° F (177 ° C).
- Line the muffin pan with baking paper.
- Crush the bananas in a large bowl.
- Add the almond milk, maple syrup, applesauce, and mix them.
- Add whole-grain spelled flour, baking powder, and cocoa powder and mix them.
- Add the chopped walnuts.
- Pour the mixture into muffin pans.
- Cook the muffins for about 25 minutes or until when a skewer is inserted, it is clean.

17. Oatmeal and Apple Muffins

What you will need

- 1 cup unsweetened applesauce
- ¼ to ½ cup of seedless dates
- 1 cup oat milk (you can use another non-dairy milk)
- Egg substitute (2 tablespoons of flaxseed mixed with 6 tablespoons of water)
- 1 tablespoon apple cider vinegar
- ½ cup unrefined sugar
- 1 teaspoon cinnamon
- 1 ½ cups oat flakes
- ½ cup raisins
- 1½ cup whole grain wheat flour
- ¾ teaspoon baking soda
- 1 teaspoon baking powder

Process

- The oven should be preheated to 300-375 ° F (191 ° C).
- Puree with 1/4 to 1/2 cup of seedless dates with 1 cup of applesauce (depending on the desired sweetness).

- Mix the linseed with water in a large bowl. Applesauce, milk, sugar, raisins, and vinegar are added; blend well. Add the oatmeal, stir and set aside until all is combined.
- Place the flour, baking soda, and baking powder into a separate bowl. Apply it to the mixture of apple and oatmeal and whisk until all is combined.
- Pour the mixture into a lightly oiled silicone muffin mold with a spoon. (If you're using a regular muffin pan, cupcake papers should be used).
- Bake the muffins till they are ready for 20 to 25 minutes.

18.Pancake cake

Beautiful and delicious pancake cake using cashew-buckwheat ricotta and chocolate-date cream as layers along with fresh mango, strawberries, and blueberries.

What you will need

- 3.5 ounces (100 g) of soaked millet
- 3.5 oz (100 g) raw buckwheat, soaked
- 7 ounces (200 ml) non-dairy milk
- 8.8 ounces (250 ml) of water

- 1 heaped tablespoon of peanut butter
- 1 pinch of sea salt
- 1 teaspoon cinnamon

RICOTTA CREAM

- 1.8 oz (50 g) raw buckwheat, soaked
- 1 cup soaked cashews
- 1 banana
- 1 teaspoon vanilla extract
- 5 drops of rum essence
- 1 pinch of sea salt
- Juice of half a small lemon
- 3.5 ounces (100 ml) of water or non-dairy milk

CHOCOLATE CREAM

- 1 cup dates
- ¾ cup of water
- 3 tablespoons cocoa powder (or half cocoa + half carob)
- 1 pinch of sea salt

Process

- Dip the millet and buckwheat overnight or during the day. Drain and rinse them.
- Combine all the ingredients in a blender and mix until it forms a paste without lumps.

- You'll get eleven 7.9-inch (20 cm) pancakes from this dough. You'll use nine for the cake.

RICOTTA CREAM

- Dip the buckwheat overnight or all day and the cashews for at least 2 hours. Drain and rinse them.
- Combine all the ingredients in a blender and mix until it forms a thick ricotta cream. You will need to help yourself with a spoon. Add the liquid gradually and only as much as it is necessary to combine all the ingredients well.
- Transfer the mixture into a bowl and set it aside.

CHOCOLATE CREAM

- Cut the dates into smaller pieces and let them soak in ¾ cup of water for at least 30 minutes.
- Mix dates, soaking water, salt, and cocoa to get a smooth cream. You will have to collect the mixture with a spoon from time to time.

MOUNTING THE PANQUEQUES CAKE

- Take a cake plate and place the first pancake.

- 1st layer: place 2 tablespoons of chocolate cream on the pancake and add another pancake on top. Do not press.
- 2nd layer: in the pancake, distribute 2 tablespoons of cashew ricotta and place another pancake on top.
- 3rd and 4th layer: repeat steps 2 and 3.
- 5th layer: cover the pancake with strawberry and mango slices and fill the holes with cashew nut ricotta cream. Put a pancake on it.
- 6th layer: spread 2 tablespoons of cashew ricotta in the pancake and place another pancake on top.
- 7th layer: place 2 tablespoons of chocolate cream on the pancake and place another pancake on top.
- 8th layer: in the pancake, distribute 2 tablespoons of cashew ricotta and place the last pancake on top.
- Put the chocolate cream on the last pancake and cross the cake for at least 6 hours in the refrigerator.
- When the cake remains in the refrigerator, the liquid will appear on the plate; Sip it with a straw before starting to cut the cake.
- Decorate the cake with fresh berries, and you're ready to serve!

19. Vegan breakfast sausages with apples and shiitakes

What you will need

- 3 tablespoons ground chia seeds + 6 tablespoons water
- 2 cups of soy curls
- ½ cup shiitake mushrooms
- ½ cup of apples finally cut
- 1 can of 15 ounces (425 grams) of navy white beans or any other white beans
- 2 tablespoons maple syrup
- ½ teaspoon of natural maple flavoring
- 1 teaspoon ground sage
- 1 teaspoon fennel seeds (I crush them a little in a seed grinder for more flavor)
- 2 teaspoons onion powder
- 1 tablespoon tamari
- ½ teaspoon red chili flakes

Process

- Cover the soy curls with fresh water and let them soak for 10 minutes.
- Mix the chia with water and set it aside.
- Lining the pan with parchment paper.
- Preheat the oven to 350 ° F (177 ° C).
- Remove the stems of the mushrooms (keep them for the broth), cut the mushrooms into large pieces

and saute them in water until they are tender and most of the water has evaporated.

- Drain the onion curls and squeeze as much water as you can.
- Drain and rinse the beans.
- Add the remaining mushrooms and ingredients, with the exception of apples, to a food processor and press until combined, while maintaining a thick consistency.
- Add the apples.
- Model the mixture into logs, each 3 inches (8 cm) long and 1 inch (3 cm) in diameter.
- Put them on the baking sheet and cook for 30 minutes, turning once or twice to make sure they are evenly distributed in color and heat. Watch out! The sausages will be very fragile until they are cooked.

20.Zucchini and oatmeal muffins

What you will need

- 1 tablespoon ground chia seeds
- 3 tablespoons of water
- 1 cup unsweetened almond milk
- 1 tablespoon lemon juice

- 1 teaspoon vanilla
- 1 cup gluten-free flour mix (for example, from the Trader Joe brand)
- ¾ cup gluten-free oatmeal (create yours by grinding oat flakes in the blender)
- ½ cup flaked gluten-free oatmeal
- ½ cup unprocessed or unrefined sugar (for example, Sucanat or turbinado)
- 2 teaspoons baking powder
- 1 teaspoon baking soda
- 1 teaspoon pumpkin pie spice
- ½ teaspoon of sea salt
- 1 ½ cups grated zucchini
- ½ cup raisins
- ½ cup walnuts, chopped

Process

- Preheat the oven to 350 ° F (177 ° C)
- Line a mold for 12 muffins with paper coverings.
- In a small bowl, combine the ground chia seeds with water and let the mixture stand.
- In a medium bowl, combine the almond milk with the lemon juice and let the mixture stand. Don't panic if it starts to set - you are supposed to!

- Mix the flours, corn flakes, sugar, baking powder, baking soda, salt and pumpkin pie spice in a large bowl.
- Add vanilla and chia seeds to the almond milk and lemon juice mixture and beat until everything is combined.
- Add the wet ingredients to the dry ones and mix them until they are combined.
- Add zucchini, raisins, and nuts. Let the dough rest for 5-10 minutes before filling the muffin pan.
- Cook everyone from 21 to 23 minutes. Once the muffins have come out of the oven, wait 2-3 minutes before transferring them to the rack to cool them.

21.Blueberry Muffins

What you will need

- ½ cup (3.2 oz or 90 g) of millet
- ½ cup (2.8 oz or 80 g) buckwheat, unroasted half-grind
- ⅓ of 2.8 oz (80 ml) cup of oat milk or rice
- 1 teaspoon applesauce
- 1 tablespoon (1.4 oz or 40 g) heaped with peanut butter

- 1 large, ripe banana
- 2 teaspoons baking powder
- ¾ cup (3.5 oz or 100 g) blueberries, fresh or frozen
- 1 pinch of sea salt

Process

- Dip millet and buckwheat overnight (or all day) in separate containers. Wash them and drain them (you can use a strainer).
- Heat the oven to 350 ° F (177 ° C).
- Put the ingredients, except the baking powder and blueberries, in the blender and mix them until a homogeneous dough forms. Do not worry; It is supposed to be quite liquid since millet inflates considerably.
- Now, mix the baking powder. In the end, combine (DON'T BID) blueberries.
- Divide the dough into 8 muffin pans and bake for 30 to 33 minutes, until golden brown.
- Let them cool for 10 minutes.

22.Smoked Tempeh Bacon

What you will need

- 1 package of 8 ounces (227 g) of tempeh (usually comes gluten-free, but check the package)
- ¼ cup of tamari or soy sauce (gluten-free, if necessary)
- 2 teaspoons of liquid smoke
- 3 tablespoons maple syrup

Process

- Steam a block of tempeh in a basket for steaming (on the stove 10 minutes or in the microwave for approximately 6 minutes).
- In a medium bowl, add all the marinade ingredients and blend well.
- Let the tempeh cool down, then cut it into strips. Place the slices in the mixture and let them marinate. The longer you leave them, the stronger the flavor will be. I like to leave them in the refrigerator overnight if possible, but at least it is necessary to do so for 30 minutes.
- Add the strips to the pan with a little marinated liquid and cook them over medium-high heat until they are crispy on one side. Turn them and brown them on the other side. Add more marinated liquid and cook until caramelized. Approximately 5 minutes per side is a reasonable estimate.

What you will need

- 1 cup chickpea flour
- 1 tablespoon of flaxseed
- ½ teaspoon salt
- ½ teaspoon general mixed seasoning
- ½ heaped teaspoon of dried mixed herbs
- ½ teaspoon baking powder
- ¼ teaspoon baking soda
- Half ahead of a small or medium cauliflower (equal to 1 grated cup)
- 1 cup of water
- ½ zucchini cut into thin half-moons
- ½ red onion cut into thin slices
- 1 large sprig of fresh rosemary, chopped into large pieces

Process

- Mix the dry ingredients and set aside.
- Cut the courgettes and onions and set aside.
- Grate or process the cauliflower (to a consistency similar to that of rice) and add it to the dry mixture, then add the water and mix well.

- Next, add the onion, courgettes, and rosemary. The mixture should be dense and lumpy, but it should be easy to pour into a mold. I used a silicone pony mold of 8 inches (20 cm), but you could also use a metal mold with a removable base. This would fit in a cake pan, but I don't know how to extract it from the plate.
- Press the mixture firmly into the mold, but leave the top rather irregular to achieve a pleasant texture.
- Bake at 350 ° F (177 ° C) for approximately 30 minutes until the top looks good and golden brown.
- Serve hot or cold.

24.Pumpkin Vegan French Toast

What you will need

- 8-10 slices of dense whole wheat bread
- ¾ cup of pumpkin puree
- 1½ cups unsweetened non-dairy milk
- 1 tablespoon maple syrup
- 1 tablespoon ground flaxseed
- 1 teaspoon cinnamon
- ¼ teaspoon nutmeg
- ¼ teaspoon of turmeric
- 1 pinch ground cloves

Process

- Beat all the ingredients in the mixture in a deep bowl.
- Heat a nonstick skillet.
- Soak each slice briefly in the mixture and drain the excess. Do not let it soak! It will make the bread too soaked.
- Cook until the bottom is golden. Turn and cook until the other side is also golden. If it seems that the interior is not cooking fast enough as the exterior is cooking, lower the heat a little.

25.Eggplant bacon

What you will need

- 1 medium eggplant
- 2 tablespoons nutritional yeast
- 3 tablespoons date paste or maple syrup
- 2 teaspoons of liquid smoke
- 2 tablespoons low sodium tamari
- 3 teaspoons onion powder
- 1 teaspoon garlic powder
- 1 tablespoon of water

Process

- Use the convection option if necessary to preheat the oven to 325 degrees F.
- Line with baking paper a large baking sheet.
- Longitudinally cut the eggplant in half. Then cut again in half lengthwise the resulting bits.
- Then cut the eggplant into long strips, use a sharp knife or mandolin.
- Prepare the sauce by adding all the ingredients in a small container and beating them until they mix well.
- Use a kitchen brush to cover both sides of the eggplant slices with the sauce.
- Place the eggplant slices on top of the baking sheet with baking paper in a single layer.
- Bake for 25-30 minutes (turning the slices in half-cooked) or until the eggplant is dry and slightly crispy.
- Take out of the oven and enjoy.

26.Buckwheat Waffles

Frozen cherries are preferable for this recipe since they melt in delicious syrup. These waffles make a great breakfast plate for the weekend.

What you will need

Waffles

- 1 cup buckwheat flour
- 1 cup whole grain wheat flour
- 1 tablespoon baking powder
- 1 teaspoon baking soda
- 1 pinch of salt
- 1 pinch of cinnamon
- 2 flaxseed eggs (see tips)
- 2 tablespoons 100% maple syrup
- 1 ½ cups of vegetable milk
- 3 tablespoons applesauce

Syrup

- 2 cups black cherries without pepas
- 3 tablespoons 100% maple syrup

Process

Preparation Of Waffles

- Place in a bowl all ingredients and combine until well combined. Stiff, thick and not too dry, should be the flour. Apply a little more vegetable milk if it's too dry.
- Heat to extreme heat the waffle maker.

- Pour batter into the waffle machine for two minutes to make waffles and cooking.
- Move yourself to a plate. If it sticks, extract the mixture from the waffle maker using a flat knife.

Sirope Preparation

- Mix all the ingredients of the syrup in a casserole. Place it in this one until it's dry. Pour the syrup over the waffles that were baked.

27.Baked ripe bananas

One of the most common foods in tropical climates, banana, is incredibly versatile and relatively simple to prepare. Larger than bananas, bananas can be consumed either green or yellow and can be found in most market stores.

What you will need

- 2 ripe bananas (dark yellow to dark brown)
- 1 teaspoon salt (only if it boils)
- Ground cinnamon

Process

If You Prepare Them In Oven

- Preheat the oven to 300-350 ° F (177 ° C). Cover a baking sheet with parchment.
- Slightly cut the peel of each banana, from top to bottom, and then peel them.
- Cut each banana into three equal parts and then cut it lengthwise into slices of ¼ to ½ inches (6 to 12 mm).
- Place the banana slices on a lined baking sheet. Sprinkle with cinnamon.
- Bake for 10 to 15 minutes, turn the bananas and bake for an additional 5 minutes.
- Serve hot.

If You Prepare Them In Stove

- Wash the bananas, but not the peels.
- Cut each banana (with its peel) into three equal parts.
- Boil a large pot of water over medium-high heat. Add the bananas and a teaspoon of salt to the boiling water.
- Boil the bananas until the peels open. At this point, remove the pot from the heat and drain the water.
- Peel each banana, then cut them into smaller pieces. Season with cinnamon and serve hot.

28.Chocolate Granola

What you will need

- 8 cups of thick oat flakes
- 2 tablespoons sliced almonds (optional)
- 2 tablespoons chopped walnuts
- Dried fruit - unsweetened cherries or raisins
- ¼-½ cup cocoa or cocoa powder
- 1 teaspoon cinnamon
- 1 cup freeze-dried, dried fruit - strawberries, mango, banana (optional)

Wet Ingredients

- 3 ripe bananas (3 bananas) or 3 cups of mango
- 1 cup dried seedless dates
- ½ cup of water
- 1 teaspoon vanilla extract
- ¼ teaspoon of sea salt

Process

- Combine the dry ingredients (except dried fruits) in a large jar.
- In a mixer, combine the wet ingredients.
- Replace the dry ones with the wet ingredients.
- Mix well and spread over a sheet of baking.
- Bake for about 8 hours at 170 degrees F (77 degrees C). I bake it overnight, and the granola is ready in the morning.
- Put off the oven and leave to cool the tray in the oven.
- With your hand or a spatula, break the granola a little.
- In a jar, add the granola and blend with the lyophilized dried fruit.
- Pack with a lid in a sealed container.

29.Tex-Mex tofu scramble

What you will need

- 28 ounces extra-firm tofu, drained (2 packages)
- ½ teaspoon of turmeric
- Herbamare or salt and pepper to taste
- 1 teaspoon oregano

- ½ teaspoon liquid smoke - "liquid smoke."
- ½ cup chopped onion
- ½ cup diced red/orange peppers
- 5 crushed garlic cloves
- 1 cup mushrooms, sliced
- ¼ cup corn (corn)
- 2 cups kale or spinach, chopped
- ¼ cup Mexican sauce
- 1 cup grape tomatoes chopped in half
- coriander to taste (optional)

Process

- Drain the tofu and cut it into small cubes.
- Cook in a wok or large skillet for one 15-20 minutes until the tofu dries (it can drain a couple of times).
- Marinate the tofu with salt and pepper or Herbamare, turmeric, oregano, and liquid smoke and cook for 5 minutes.
- Add the onion, peppers, and garlic and cook for 3 minutes.
- Add the mushrooms, corn, and ground beef substitute and cook for 2 minutes.
- Add the kale or spinach and sauce.
- Simmer for 3 minutes.
- Pour and serve with the grape tomatoes and cilantro. Enjoy your meal!

What you will need

- 1 ¼ cups unsweetened almond milk
- ½ cup oatmeal
- 1 tablespoon almond butter
- 1 tablespoon coconut flakes
- 1 banana
- ¾ cup of red fruits
- 1 teaspoon millet sprouts (optional)
- 1 teaspoon raw cocoa nibs (optional)
- Dried edible flowers (optional)

Process

- Soak the oatmeal in almond milk for about 10 minutes.
- While the oatmeal is soaking, heat a small pan and toast the coconut flakes until golden brown.
- Crush the banana (save some slices from decorating).
- Add the mashed banana, soaked oatmeal, roasted coconut flakes, and the rest of the ingredients to a pot and boil.

- Simmer for 4 to 5 minutes, stirring constantly.
- Transfer everything to a bowl and cover it with banana slices, red fruits, millet sprouts, cocoa nibs, and dried edible flowers.

CHAPTER THREE
Plant-based diet dessert recipes

31.Apple "Halloween" lamps

Adorable and easy to prepare, these apple and peanut butter lanterns are a delicious breakfast, snack, or snack for Halloween.

What you will need

- 6 red apples
- 1 cup peanut butter
- 1 tablespoon date paste
- ½ teaspoon of pumpkin pie spice
- 1 cup of oil-free granola

Process

- Preheat the oven to 300-350 ° F (177 ° C).
- Cut the top of each apple.
- Take out the inside with a spoon or a melon. Make sure the walls are thick.
- Carefully carve the face of the flashlight to make eyes and mouth.
- Melt peanut butter in a saucepan until smooth and smooth.
- In a bowl, combine melted peanut butter with date paste and pumpkin spices.

- Fill the apples with the peanut butter mixture and replace the apple tops.
- Bake the apples on a baking sheet for 10 minutes.
- Place the granola in the apples and bake for another 10 minutes.
- Serve immediately.

32.Matcha bars without baking with chocolate and coconut

What you will need

- 1 cup oatmeal
- ½ cup raw cashews
- ⅓ cup coconut flour
- ½ cup nut butter
- 1 cup coconut milk lite
- 4 tablespoons matcha powder
- 2 tablespoons raw cocoa powder
- 2 tablespoons unsweetened coconut flakes
- 2 tablespoons maple syrup
- ½ teaspoon coconut extract
- ½ teaspoon cinnamon

Process

- Mix oats and cashews in a food processor (I use my Vitamix) to produce the finest possible quality.
- Place in a large bowl the mixture.
- Melt the almond butter in the microwave and blend it with the mixture for about 30 seconds.
- Add the remaining ingredients and mix well.
- Cover a rectangular container or tray (preferably with some depth so that the bars are not too thin) with baking paper.
- Add the mixture into the bowl. Flatten it as much as you can.
- Sprinkle the dressings you want - I added a little more grated coconut and matcha to mine - but you can add some peanut butter, chocolate chips, nuts, etc.
- cool the mixture for a few hours or until ready.
- Cut it into bars and enjoy!

33.Superfood in chocolate chip cookies

What you will need

- ½ cup peanut butter
- ½ cup of soy milk
- 8 Medjool dates
- 1 cup almond flour

- 1 cup oatmeal
- 1 cup oatmeal
- ¼ cup ground flaxseed
- ½ cup goji berries
- ½ cup of cocoa beans
- 1 ripe banana
- 1 tablespoon vanilla

Process

- Put in a food processor all ingredients and mix until well combined.
- Place the mixture tablespoons on a parchment paper-lined cookie sheet.
- Use another sheet of parchment paper to press the mixture down.
- Bake for 20 minutes at 350 ° F (176 ° C).

34.Almond cookies with jam footprint

These cookies melt in your mouth and can be filled with your favorite jam for a delicious dessert.

What you will need

- 1 cup oatmeal
- ½ cup almond flour
- 6 tablespoons date sugar
- 2 tablespoons ground flaxseed

- ½ teaspoon baking powder
- ¼ teaspoon baking soda
- ½ teaspoon ground cinnamon
- a pinch of sea salt
- ½ cup unsweetened dairy-free milk
- ¼ cup fruit-sweetened jam

Process

- Preheat the oven to 350 F.
- Line with parchment paper a baking sheet.
- Mix oatmeal, almond meal, date sugar, flaxseed, baking powder, baking soda, cinnamon, and salt in a mixing bowl.
- Add the milk depending on the plant and mix the dough well with a spoon or your hands. It is meant to be dense but not too sticky. Apply a little more oatmeal if it's too wet and blend well.
- Oatmeal and thoroughly blend.
- Place the remaining dough on the baking sheet lined with baking paper and place the balls at a distance of around 1 to 2 inches.
- To build a well to contain the jam, press the center of each cookie with your thumb.
- Fill each "footprint" of the cookies with ¼ teaspoon of jam.
- Bake the cookies until lightly browned, about 30 minutes.

- Transfer the baking sheet to a cooling rack for a few minutes.

35. Vegan Chocolate Ice Cream

This delicious chocolate ice cream is healthy and the perfect way to satisfy your cravings for something sweet. It is vegan and free of refined sugar. To prepare it, you do not need any machinery or special container for ice cream.

What you will need

- 3 frozen bananas
- ¼ cup unsweetened almond milk
- 3 tablespoons cocoa or cocoa powder
- ¼-½ teaspoon cinnamon powder (optional)

Process

- Place frozen bananas and almond milk in a food processor or blender.
- Process well until silky.
- Add the cocoa and cinnamon.
- Process until well mixed
- Place the ice cream in the freezer for 15-20 minutes
- Consume immediately.

36. Ginger cookies

What you will need

- 3 cups white wholemeal flour
- 1 teaspoon allspice
- 2 teaspoons ginger
- 1 teaspoon of cloves
- 2 teaspoons cinnamon
- 1 teaspoon baking soda
- ¼ teaspoon of sea salt
- 2 tablespoons applesauce
- ¼ cup of sugar on the date
- ¼ cup of sugar on the date
- ¼ cup dark molasses
- ½ cup date pasta
- 1 flaxseed egg (optional)
- ¼ cup of cold water
- 1 teaspoon vanilla
- 1-2 tablespoons cold water (as needed

Process

- Preheat the oven to 350 degrees F.
- Mix together the dry ingredients. Leave aside.
- Mix applesauce, date sugar, date paste, molasses, and flaxseed egg (flax) well.
- Add ¼ cup of cold water and vanilla.
- Add the dry ingredients to the bowl containing the wet ingredients and mix until a thick dough is

obtained. Add cold water (1-2 tablespoons) until the dough sticks well.

- Stretch the dough until it is ¼ inch wide.
- Cut shapes with a cookie cutter and transfer it to a baking sheet lined with baking paper.
- Bake for 15 minutes. Let cool.

37.Drunk chocolate cake with mousse and strawberries

What you will need

- 3 cups all-purpose gluten-free flour
- ½ cup date or coconut sugar
- 2 teaspoons baking powder
- 1 teaspoon baking soda
- ½ teaspoon of sea salt
- 6 tablespoons cocoa powder
- 4 tablespoons ground flax seeds
- 4 teaspoons vanilla extract
- 4 tablespoons unsweetened applesauce
- 2 tablespoons apple cider vinegar
- 1 cup raisins
- 2 cups of cold water

COVERAGES

- 8 cups fresh or thawed strawberries

- 4 cups of chocolate mousse

Process

- Preheat the oven to 350 degrees F.
- In a large container, combine flour, sugar, baking powder, baking soda, cocoa powder, ground flaxseed (flax), and salt.
- In a blender, mix the water and raisins well.
- Pour the raisin water mixture into a separate bowl and combine it with the vinegar, vanilla, and applesauce.
- Pour the wet ingredients over the dry ones and stir with a whisk until well mixed.
- Pour the mixture into a round baking dish covered with baking paper.
- Bake for 30 minutes.
- Remove from the oven and wait for it to cool.
- To assemble the drunk cake, start by spreading a layer of chocolate mousse at the bottom of a cake pie bowl, a round bowl, or a cup of personal size parfait.
- Cover the mousse with a layer of strawberries.
- Place a layer of cake. If you opt for a personal parfait, you can use a round cookie cutter to cut the cake.
- Repeat steps 9-11 until you fill the bowl or cup.

- The last layer should be chocolate and strawberry mousse.

38. 4-ingredient chocolate mousse

This creamy chocolate mousse carries only 4 ingredients and a fraction of the fat of the traditional mousse.

What you will need

- 2 boxes of 12.3 ounces silky tofu
- 4 tablespoons cocoa powder
- 1 teaspoon vanilla
- 1 cup date paste

Process

- Mix the tofu, cocoa powder, date paste, and vanilla in a blender until the ingredients are well incorporated.
- Store in the refrigerator before serving, and it will thicken even more.

39. Millet and buckwheat muffins with black currants

What you will need

- ½ cup (90 g) of millet

- ½ cup (80 g) of unroasted buckwheat groats
- 4 chopped figs
- ¾ cup (160 ml) oatmeal or rice milk
- 1 tablespoon applesauce
- 1 heaped tablespoon (40 g) peanut butter
- 1 large ripe banana
- 1 pinch of sea salt
- 2 heaped teaspoons of baking powder
- ¾ cup (100 g) blackcurrants, fresh or frozen

Process

- Soak millet and buckwheat overnight (or all day) in separate containers. Wash and drain (you can use a strainer).
- Soak the chopped figs in ¾ cup (160 ml) of oat milk for at least 30 minutes.
- Heat the oven to 350 ° F (177 ° C).
- Put the ingredients, except baking powder and blackcurrants, in a blender and mix them until a homogeneous lump is formed without lumps. Do not worry; It is supposed to be quite liquid since millet inflates considerably.
- Now mix the baking powder. Unplug the blender and finally combine (DON'T LIQUID) the currants with a spoon.
- Divide the dough into 9 muffin pans and bake for 33 to 35 minutes, until golden brown.

40.Apple and pumpkin pie

What you will need

- 1 spoon ground flax seeds + 2 ½ tablespoons water (flax egg)
- ½ cup all-purpose gluten-free flour (or oatmeal)
- 1 ½ cup quick-cooking oatmeal
- 1 tablespoon baking powder
- 1 teaspoon baking soda
- 2 tablespoons pumpkin pie spice
- 1 tablespoon cinnamon
- 4 medium granny smith apples
- ½ cup date pasta
- 1 cup pumpkin puree
- 1 teaspoon vanilla extract
- ¼ cup of water (optional)

Process

- Preheat the oven to 350 degrees F.
- Mix ground flaxseed (flax) seeds with water in a small bowl and set aside for 10 minutes.
- Mix all dry ingredients in a large bowl.
- Cut the apples into thin slices and place them in a container.

- Add the pumpkin puree, vanilla extract, flaxseed with water, and date paste to apples and mix well.
- merge the dry ingredients with the apples and mix well. Add water if the mixture seems to be too dry.
- Place the mixture in an 8 x 11 (2 quarts) container suitable for baking and bake for 30-35 minutes.

41. Banana bread with cherries and chocolate chips

What you will need

- 2 cups white whole wheat flour
- 1 teaspoon baking soda
- 1 teaspoon baking powder
- 2 ripe bananas, crushed
- 1 cup non-dairy milk (I use unsweetened soy milk)
- ½ cup maple syrup
- 1½ teaspoon vanilla extract
- ½ cup dairy-free chocolate chips
- 1 cup frozen cherries, frozen, thawed

Process

- Set aside 5 tiny bread molds (each 3 x 6 inches or 8 x 15 centimeters), or line 12 cups of muffins with baking paper.

- In a big bowl, stir the flour, baking soda, and baking powder. In a medium bowl, mix the bananas, milk, maple syrup, and vanilla. mix the wet ingredients to the dry ones and mix them until they are almost combined. Add the chocolate chips and cherries.
- Fill baking trays or pans muffins evenly. Bake the bread for 24 to 28 minutes. Bake the muffins for 18 to 24 minutes or until golden brown, and when you insert a toothpick in the center, it comes out clean.
- Remove the bread or muffins from the oven and transfer them to the rack to cool.

42. Iced lemon pie with pineapple and fresh blueberries

What you will need

- ¼ cup fresh lemon juice (about 2 lemons)
- ¼ cup of water
- 1 cup fresh pineapple, chopped
- ¼ teaspoon grated lemon peel
- ¼ cup fresh blueberries, rinsed and completely dried

Process

- Add fresh juice, water, pineapple and grated lemon peel to a high-speed blender. Process them until they run out of lumps.
- Pour the mixture carefully into the container of an automatic ice cream maker and process it according to the manufacturer's instructions.
- Add fresh berries during the last 10 minutes. Enjoy immediately, or let it harden further in the freezer for an hour or more.

43.Chocolate chip gelato

What you will need

- 2 cups dairy-free milk
- ¾ cup pure maple syrup
- 1 tablespoon pure vanilla extract
- ⅓ semi-sweet vegan chocolate chips, finely chopped or flaked

Process

- Beat dairy-free milk, maple syrup, and vanilla together in a large bowl until well combined.

- Pour the mixture carefully into the container of an automatic ice cream maker and process it according to the manufacturer's instructions.
- During the last 10 or 15 minutes, add the chopped chocolate and continue processing until the desired texture is achieved. Enjoy the gelato immediately, or let it harden further in the freezer for an hour or more.

44.Peanut butter and jelly ice cream

What you will need

- 2 cups dairy-free milk, simple, sugar-free
- ⅔ cup maple syrup
- 3 tablespoons creamy natural peanut butter
- ½ teaspoon ground ginger
- 2 teaspoons pure vanilla extract
- 6 tablespoons canned fruits

Process

- Beat the milk without milk, maple syrup, peanut butter, and vanilla in a large bowl until well combined. Pour the mixture carefully into the container of an automatic ice cream maker and process it according to the manufacturer's instructions.

- Add canned fruits for the last 10 minutes, and let them combine with the ice cream until the desired texture is achieved. Enjoy the ice cream immediately, or let it harden further in the freezer for an hour or more.

45.Peanut Butter Banana Cookies

What you will need

- 10 Medjool dates, seeded
- 1 ripe banana (too mature is beautiful)
- ½ cup peanut butter
- ¼ cup unsweetened applesauce
- 1 teaspoon vanilla extract
- 2½ cups of quick-cooked or flaked oatmeal
- ¼ cup whole grain wheat flour for pastries
- ¼ teaspoon baking powder

Process.

- Add dates to a small pan with enough water to cover and cook for 5 minutes over medium heat. Next, turn the mixture into a puree in a food processor until it is lump-free and creamy.

- Add the banana, peanut butter, applesauce, and vanilla to the food processor and puree them until lump-free and creamy.
- Transfer the peanut butter and banana mixture to a bowl and add the remaining ingredients, stirring them only until they are combined.
- Using a small scoop of ice cream or a tablespoon, place tablespoons of dough on a baking sheet with parchment, silicone, or non-stick lining.
- Bake large cookies for about 15 minutes and small cookies for about 12 minutes. Cookies should be lightly browned on top.
- Let the cookies stand for about 10 minutes before removing them from the baking sheet, so it will be easier to remove them. Transfer them to a wire rack to cool completely.

46. Oatmeal breakfast muffins

These compact and moist muffins are like eating oatmeal coated with bananas and raisins in a bowl, and only these can be eaten directly with your hands!

What you will need

- 2½ cups of flaked oatmeal
- ½ cup oatmeal
- 1 teaspoon baking powder

- ½ teaspoon baking soda
- ½ teaspoon salt
- 1 tablespoon cinnamon
- ½ teaspoon ground nutmeg
- 4 ripe bananas, crushed
- 1 grated apple
- ½ cup non-dairy milk
- 2 teaspoons vanilla extract
- ½ cup raisins
- ½ cup chopped walnuts (optional)

Process

- Preheat the oven to 300-350 ° F (177 ° C).
- In a large bowl, combine and beat the dry ingredients.
- In a small bowl, combine bananas, apple, non-dairy milk, vanilla, and stir until well combined.
- mix the wet ingredients to the dry ones and combine them well. Add raisins and nuts, if you use them.
- If you use a mold for 6 muffins, bake for 45 minutes. If you use a mold of 12 muffins bake for 35 minutes.

47.Oatmeal and Apple Cookies

These very healthy cookies are simple and delicious - you use only 5 ingredients and need only 5 minutes to put them together!

What you will need

- 2 cups gluten-free oatmeal
- 2 cups applesauce
- ½ cup raisins
- 1½ tablespoons chia seeds
- 2 teaspoons cinnamon

Process

- Preheat to 350 ° F (177 ° C) in the oven.
- In a medium bowl, put all 5 ingredients and stir until combined. Let stand during the heating of the oven for 10 minutes.
- Serve big spoonfuls of the mixture (covered in baking paper) on the cookie sheet. Gently flatten and spread the mixture to the size and shape you want with the back of the spoon. Bake for about 25 minutes.
- After removal from the oven, move the cookies to the rack to cool.

- Don't try to eat them once!

48.Blackberry and lemon muffins for tea

What you will need

- 2 cups whole grain wheat flour for baking
- ½ cup of Sucanat (refined cane sugar)
- 1½ teaspoon baking powder
- 1 teaspoon grated lemon peel
- ½ cup natural soy yogurt
- 1 cup non-dairy milk
- 1 tablespoon lemon juice
- 2 egg substitutes (2 tablespoons ground flaxseed with 6 tablespoons water)
- 1 cup blackberries
- 2 tablespoons coconut with reduced-fat and sugar-free content (optional)

Process

- Preheat to 350 ° F (177 ° C) in the oven.
- Fill a paper-coated mold for 12 muffins (or use a non-stick skillet).
- In a medium bowl, mix flour, sucanat sweetener, baking powder, and rubbed lemon peel.

- In a separate bowl, mix soy yogurt, milk, lemon juice, and egg substitutes.
- Pour into the dry mixture the wet mixture and stir until it is hot.
- Carefully add blackberries.
- In the prepared muffin pan, distribute the mixture evenly.
- Sprinkle the coconut (optional) on top of the muffins.
- Bake them for 45 minutes in the preheated oven or until one of them has a toothpick inserted in the middle. Until serving, let them cool slightly.

49.Walnut Butter Brownies

These are extra-wet whole grain brownies and have no added oil. Nut butter and applesauce give a caramel-like texture for a very special chocolate treat.

What you will need

- 2 tablespoons ground flaxseed
- 6 tablespoons warm water
- ½ cup of Sucanat (unrefined cane sugar)
- ½ cup agave nectar
- 1 teaspoon vanilla extract
- ¼ cup nut butter
- ½ cup unsweetened applesauce

- ¾ cup whole grain wheat flour for pastry
- ⅓ cup unsweetened cocoa powder
- ½ teaspoon baking powder
- ¼ teaspoon of sea salt
- ½ cup vegan and semi-sweet chocolate chips

Process

- Preheat to 350 ° F (177 ° C) in the oven. Line a pan with baking paper measuring 9x 9 inches (23x 23 cm) and set aside.
- Mix flour and water in a small pan. Let 2 minutes stand.
- Combine the Sucanat, agave, cinnamon, nut butter, applesauce, and flaxseed flour mixture into a separate bowl until smooth.
- Combine food, chocolate, baking powder, and salt in a third pan. Apply all to the mixture of Sucanat and stir to combine.
- Add the chips of vegan chocolate.
- Place the dough in the tub.
- Bake until a toothpick inserted in the middle comes out clean for 30 to 35 minutes.
- Until cutting, let it cool on a wire rack.

50.Fruit and date cake, incredibly delicious

What you will need

- 1 cup seedless dates
- 1½ cups walnuts (or pecans)
- 1 teaspoon vanilla extract
- ½ cup shredded coconut
- ½ teaspoon cinnamon
- Fresh sliced fruit for coverage

Process

- Mix all the ingredients in the crust in a high-speed food processor until paste forms.
- Press the dough into a cake pan and cool it until it is ready for the fruit to be added.
- Place the fruit on top of the cake.
- Chill for 1 hour before serving.

51.Cherry and poppy seed muffins

What you will need

DRY

- 1 cup (120 g) raw buckwheat flour
- 1 ¼ cup oatmeal (155 g) oatmeal
- 2 tablespoons poppy seeds
- 2 teaspoons cinnamon

- ½ teaspoon cardamom
- 2 teaspoons baking powder

Wet

- 10 chopped figs
- A little more than 1 cup (260 ml) of vegetable milk, without sugar
- 2 ripe bananas
- 2 heaped tablespoons unsweetened applesauce
- 2 tablespoons peanut butter
- 1 pinch of sea salt (optional)
- ½ cup (50 g) dark chocolate (at least 70% cocoa), chopped
- 24 fresh or frozen cherries

Process

- Preheat the oven to 355 ° F (180 ° C).
- Cut the figs and soak them in the vegetable milk for at least half an hour. If you soak them more, place them in the fridge.
- While the figs are soaking, finely chop the chocolate and set aside. Combine all other dry ingredients in a bowl. Place the figs and milk in the blender. Add all remaining wet ingredients and mix until smooth.
- Pour the wet mixture over the dry ingredients and mix well. Make sure there are no lumps. Now add the chopped chocolate.

- Fill molds 12 muffins (I molds using silicone) with the mass and finally hits two cherries on each muffin.
- Bake for 25 to 30 minutes. Let them cool a little before trying to remove them from the molds.

52.Homemade granola

What you will need

- 3 cups flaked oatmeal
- ¼ cup chopped raw nuts
- ¼ cup raw pecans, chopped
- ¼ cup raw almonds, chopped
- ½ cup pure maple syrup
- 2 teaspoons vanilla
- 2 teaspoons cinnamon
- 1 pinch of salt (optional)

Process

- Preheat the oven to 250-300 ° F (149 ° C).
- Put all ingredients in a bowl, mix well, and cover everything with maple syrup. Spread the mixture on a baking sheet or broiler pan.
- Bake for 30-40 minutes with occasional stirring until the mixture turns brown. Move the top plate to the

wire rack and let it cool completely. Refrigerate the granola in a sealed jar.

53.Tofu cashew cheesecake dessert

What you will need

For The Mass

- 1 cup soaked cashews
- 6 ounces (175 g) of soft tofu
- 1 tablespoon peanut butter
- 1 small banana
- A handful of grated coconut
- 1 pinch of sea salt
- 1 ounce (30 ml) of water
- 2 tablespoons raw cocoa powder (mix it in half the dough)

The Swirl

- 1 tablespoon peanut butter

- 1 teaspoon agave syrup

End Mix

- 3 tablespoons of raisins, dipped in rum
- 4 chopped figs

Process

- Soak the raisins in rum (not mandatory). (Of course, discard rum from children's containers). Soak the cashews in water for 2 to 2.5 hours. Rinse and drain.
- Enter the dough ingredients (except cocoa powder) in the blender. Mix them until a uniform dough forms.
- Now, put half of the mixture in a bowl and add the cocoa powder to the remaining half in the blender.
- Mix half of the raisins and chopped figs in the brown dough and the other half in the white dough.
- Prepare the swirl by mixing peanut butter (at room temperature) and agave syrup.
- Now, start compiling the containers. Put the brown and white dough in the bowls in turns. Add small balls of butter mixture everywhere.
- When you reach the last layer, add about 5 peanut butter balls on top. Now, it's all about your creativity and artistic skills. Take a sushi stick and make some cute swirls on top of the dessert.

- Place the desserts in the fridge for a few hours. Cover the containers with foil if you need to keep them longer.

54. Christmas nut cake with ginger

What you will need

MASS MIX

- ½ cup unroasted buckwheat
- ½ cup of millet
- ⅓ cup (80 ml) unsweetened oat milk
- 1 ripe banana
- 1 tablespoon peanut butter
- 1 pinch of sea salt
- ½ teaspoon of turmeric
- ½ to 1 teaspoon of gingerbread spices
- 2 tablespoons baking powder (add them at the end)

TO COMBINE WITH MIXED MASS

- ¼ cup chopped hazelnuts
- ¼ cup chopped almonds
- ¼ cup chopped walnuts
- ¼ cup dried apricots, chopped
- ¼ cup raisins dipped in rum

- 5 chopped figs
- ⅛ cup goji berries
- 2 tablespoons grated orange peel or sugary orange peel (use organic)
- ¼ cup 50g (1.8oz) dark chocolate, chopped

Process

- Soak millet and buckwheat overnight (or throughout the day) in water in separate containers. Clean and drain them (you can use a strainer).
- Soak the raisins in a mixture of rum and hot water (half and a half) overnight. You can discard the soaking liquid later, or you can replace it with some of the oat milk in the recipe.
- Chop everything that needs to be cut from the second table.
- Heat the oven to 350 ° F (177 ° C) and line a bread pan with baking paper.
- Place the ingredients in the mixed dough, except for the baking powder, in a blender, and mix them until a uniform dough forms. Do not worry; It is supposed to be quite liquid since millet inflates considerably.
- Now, add the baking powder.
- Finally, combine (DO NOT LIQUUS) chopped nuts, dried fruits, and chocolate.

- Pour the dough into a bread pan and bake for 40 to 45 minutes until your Christmas cake is golden brown.
- Let cool before cutting and serving. If you leave the mold on the counter, cover it with a clean dishcloth or foil (loosely) to keep the cake moist.

55.Chocolate bark

Chia, sesame, and pumpkin seeds give life to this easy but fantastic vegan chocolate dessert along with hazelnuts, pistachios, orange slices, and cardamom.

What you will need

- 1 thin peel orange
- ¾ cup pistachio nuts, roasted, chilled and chopped into large pieces
- ¼ cup hazelnuts, toasted, chilled, peeled and chopped into large pieces
- ¼ cup pumpkin seeds, toasted and chilled
- 1 tablespoon chia seeds
- 1 tablespoon sesame seeds, toasted and cooled
- 1 teaspoon grated orange peel
- 1 cardamom pod, finely crushed and sieved
- 12 ounces (340 g) tempered, dairy-free dark chocolate (65% cocoa content)
- 2 teaspoons flaky sea salt

- Candy or candy thermometer

Process

- Preheat the oven to 100-150 ° F (66 ° C). Line a baking sheet with parchment paper.
- Finely slice the orange crosswise and place it on the prepared baking sheet. Bake for 2 to 3 hours until dry but slightly sticky. Remove it from the oven and let it cool.
- When they cool enough to handle them, cut the orange slices into fragments; set them aside.
- In a large bowl, mix the nuts, seeds, and grated orange peel until completely combined. Place the mixture in a single layer on a baking sheet lined with kitchen parchment. Set it aside.
- Melt the chocolate in a water bath until it reaches 88 to 90 ° F (32 to 33 ° C) and pours it over the nut mixture to cover it completely.
- When the chocolate is semi-cold but still sticky, sprinkle the surface with sea salt and pieces of orange.
- Place the mixture in a cold area of your kitchen or refrigerate until the crust cools completely, and cut it into bite-sized pieces.

What you will need

Ingredients Of Cookies

- 2 large ripe bananas
- 2 cups of flaked oatmeal
- 2 tablespoons peanut butter
- 1 pinch of sea salt
- 2 teaspoons cocoa powder (to add later)

Ingredients Of The Cream Of Marañones

- ½ cup soaked cashews
- ½ banana
- 1 teaspoon vanilla extract
- 1 pinch of sea salt
- Juice of half a small lemon
- Enough water or dairy-free milk to make the creamy smooth, but not too liquid

Ingredients Of Dates And Chocolate

- 1 cup dates
- ¾ cup of water
- 3 tablespoons cocoa powder (or half cocoa + half carob)

- 1 pinch of sea salt

Process

Preparation Of Cookies

- Puree with banana, peanut butter, and sea salt in a blender.
- In a bowl, mix peanut and banana puree with flake oatmeal.
- Heat the oven to 350 ° F (177 ° C).
- Place parchment on the top board. Take out the heart-shaped cookie cutter (or whatever you like) and place it on the top.
- Take approximately 1.2 oz (35 g) of cookie dough and press evenly with a cookie cutter. Remove the cutter with a spoon. Repeat until there are 8 cookies in the tray.
- Add 2 teaspoons of raw cocoa powder to the remaining dough. Also, add a few drops of milk without dairy and mix.
- Repeat step 5 until the fabric disappears.
- Bake cookies for 16 minutes in the center grill of the oven and let cool.

Preparation Of The Cream Of Marañones

- Soak the cashews for at least 2 hours. Drain and rinse them.

- Combine all the ingredients in a blender (as it is a very small portion, I used a chopper) and mix them until a thick cream forms. You will need a spoon to help you. Add the liquid gradually and only as much as necessary to combine all the ingredients well.
- Transfer the cream to a bowl and set it aside.

Preparation Of Dates And Chocolate

- Cut the dates into smaller pieces and let them soak in ¾ cup of water for at least 30 minutes.
- Mix dates, soaking water, salt, and cocoa, until a lump-free cream is left. You will have to pick them up with a spoon between each mixture.
- Decorate the cookies as you want. You can also use melted dark chocolate as I did.

CHAPTER FOUR
Plant-based diet Side Dishes recipes

57.Spinach Stuffed Mushrooms

A tasty filling of white beans and spinach, seasoned with garlic, onions, and white wine, will make these stuffed mushrooms a success at your next party. In fact, they are so exquisite that you will probably forget that they are also full of nutrients. It is recommended that you double the recipe because they go fast!

What you will need

- 16 oz white whole mushrooms or "crimini."
- 3 crushed garlic cloves
- ¼ cup onion, minced
- ¼ cup white wine or vegetable stock
- 3 tablespoon low sodium soy sauce or tamari
- 3 cups sweet spinach
- ¼ cup white beans
- 2 tablespoons nutritional yeast
- ¼ red pepper, minced

Process

- Preheat the oven to 375 degrees F.
- Remove the stems from the mushrooms, leave the tops intact and chop the stems.

- Sauté the onion, garlic, and mushroom stalks in a pan.
- Add the wine and the soy sauce or tamari, continue cooking for 2-3 minutes, or until the vegetables soften a little.
- Add the tender spinach and sauté for a minute.
- move the vegetable mixture to a food processor.
- Add beans and nutritional yeast and mix to combine.
- Transfer to a bowl and mix the chopped red pepper.
- Place the mushroom tops with the top side down in a baking dish.
- Fill each mushroom top with the mixture.
- Bake for 20-25 minutes.
- Remove from oven and serve hot

58.Crispy Cauliflower Chips

These crispy slices of breaded and baked cauliflower are a success. Use your favorite seasonings to create a variety of spicy, salty, or sour flavors with an appetizing crunch.

What you will need

- A head of cauliflower, cut into florets
- ½ teaspoon garlic powder
- ½ teaspoon of seasoning for poultry or seasoning without salt (optional)

- ¾ cup of aquafaba
- 1 cup gluten-free bread crumbs

Process

- Preheat the oven to 450 degrees F.
- Put the cauliflower in a container and season with the garlic powder and the seasoning for birds (or without salt). Be sure to cover the cauliflower evenly.
- Soak the cauliflower, a foil at once, in the aquafaba, and shake off the excess.
- Cover with breadcrumbs and shake off excess.
- Repeat with all cauliflower florets.
- put the florets on a baking sheet lined with baking paper.
- Bake for 15 minutes.
- Turn the florets over to bake evenly.
- Bake for another 15 minutes.
- Serve immediately.

59.Baked potatoes without oil

These crispy chips are the perfect companion for carrot burgers or hot dogs. By boiling the potatoes for a few minutes before baking, the starch level is reduced, and they provide enough moisture so that they become crispy when baked without using oil.

What you will need

- 4 medium yellow potatoes
- ½ teaspoon garlic powder
- sea salt and pepper to taste

Process

- Preheat the oven to 400 degrees F (218 degrees C).
- Cut the potatoes into sticks similar to "fries" of approximately ½ "- ¾" thick.
- Put the potatoes in a deep pot, cover with water, and boil for 5 minutes.
- Drain well and pour it into a deep container.
- Add the spices and cover the potatoes well with the seasoning.
- Put the potatoes on a baking sheet covered with a silicone foil or baking paper.
- Bake for 35-40 minutes or until cooked and crispy. Enjoy your meal!

60.Red cranberry and kale pilaf

This dish is a colorful addition to any table that has a festive dinner, either as a main course or as an accompaniment. Kale and blueberries are a delicious culinary combo and are also well matched nutritionally.

What you will need

- 1 cup of brown rice
- 1 ¾ cups vegetable stock
- 1 small yellow onion, diced
- 12 ounces (340 grams) of kale (approximately 5 cups)
- 3 or 4 cloves garlic, minced
- ½ teaspoon red pepper flakes
- ½ cup dried cranberries
- ¼ cup chopped cashews or other nuts (optional)

Process

- In a medium-sized pot or rice cooker, cook the rice in the broth according to package directions.
- Sauté the onion for five minutes, or until it is transparent.
- Add the kale (without stems and thickly chopped leaves) and cook for another five minutes, or until the kale is soft.
- Add the garlic in flakes and red pepper and cook everything for another minute.
- Add the cooked rice and continue sautéing for three minutes, or until the rice has completely warmed.
- Remove the pan from the heat.

- Add red cranberries and optional nuts, stir well.

61.Sweet potato tropical casserole

This sweet potato casserole is prepared in just minutes and is a very popular dish with adults and children.

What you will need

- 4 cups diced sweet potatoes
- 1 cup diced mango
- 1 cup diced pineapple
- ½ teaspoon unsalted garlic and herb seasoning
- ½ cup pineapple and coconut juice

Process

- Preheat oven to 350 degrees F.
- Combine all ingredients in an 8 x 11 (2 qt) baking sheet.
- Bake covered for 25 minutes.
- Bake uncovered for 5 minutes and serve.

62.Traditional stuffing

Stuffing is one of my favorite dishes for Thanksgiving dinner. This delicious filling has the same flavor of the traditional version with which you grew up but without fat.

What you will need

- ½ cup vegetable broth
- 1 spoon low sodium soy sauce or tamari
- 4 cups gluten-free or whole-wheat bread cubes
- ½ cup chopped onion
- 1 cup chopped celery
- 1 tablespoon nutritional yeast
- ½ teaspoon bird seasoning
- ½ teaspoon garlic powder
- ½ teaspoon dried parsley

Process

- Preheat the oven to 350 F.
- In a small bowl, mix the soil flax seeds with the water and set aside for 10 minutes.
- In a big bowl, combine every dry ingredient.
- Cut and place the apples in thin slices in a container.
- Add the pumpkin puree, vanilla extract, water-based flaxseed, and apple date paste and blend well.
- Combine the dry ingredients and blend well with the apples. If the mixture tends to be too dry, add water.
- In an appropriate baking dish, put the mixture and bake for 30-35 minutes.

What you will need

- ½ teaspoon sage
- 1 teaspoon thyme
- 1 teaspoon rosemary
- ½ cup wild rice
- 1 ½ cups quinoa
- 1 cup brown rice or rice mix
- ½ cup freshly squeezed orange juice
- 2 ½ cups of vegetable stock
- ½ sea salt
- 1 cup grated carrots
- 1 cup pomegranate seeds (optional)
- 1 cup gooseberries (optional)

Process

- Heat a pot over medium heat.
- Add the spices to the pot and sauté for 30 seconds.
- Add wild rice, quinoa, and brown rice and stir for 1 minute.

- Add orange juice, vegetable broth, and sea salt, and stir well.
- Bring to a boil, cover and reduce heat to medium-low and cook for 45 minutes.
- Remove from heat, add carrots and fruit, and serve.

64. Mashed sweet potato with cauliflower

What you will need

- 1 head of cauliflower, without the core and cut into pieces
- 2 large sweet potatoes, peeled and cut into pieces of 1 inch (2.5 centimeters)
- ½ cup unsweetened vegetable milk
- 1 teaspoon garlic powder
- Salt and pepper to taste

Process

- Steam the cauliflower and sweet potato in approximately 1-2 inches (2.5 - 5 centimeters) of water until soft. Alternatively, you can roast them on parchment paper in the oven at 400 ° F (204 ° C) for 20 to 30 minutes.
- Add the soft vegetables to your food processor and process everything for one minute to dissolve the

ingredients, or you can crush them by hand. Add the vegetable milk, garlic powder, salt, and pepper and continue processing until smooth.

65.Brussels sprouts caramelized with blueberries.

What you will need

- 8 chopped dates
- ½ cup of water
- 3 cups fresh Brussels sprouts, cut in half
- 1 cup fresh blueberries
- 1 tablespoon miso paste
- 1 cup low-sodium vegetable broth or water
- 1 organic red onion, chopped
- 1 tablespoon soy sauce
- ¼ cup of nuts such as almonds, Brazil nuts, several mixed, etc. (optional) Pepper to taste

Process

- In a food processor, mix dates with ½ cup of water until a creamy texture is obtained. Set it aside for a moment.
- In a saucepan over medium-high heat sauté the Brussels sprouts along with the onion, miso,

blueberries and ½ cup of broth or water. Cook covered for 10 minutes or until lightly brown.

- Stir frequently and add the rest of the additional liquid as necessary to prevent burning.
- Cook the sprouts until they are caramelized by the edges.
- Add the soy sauce, ground pepper, and date paste. Mix and match well.
- Serve and garnish with nuts.

66. Red potatoes with green vegetables

What you will need

- 4 red potatoes
- 1 bunch of seasonal green vegetables (kale, Swiss chard, kale, etc.)
- ½ teaspoon black pepper
- 1 onion cut into thin slices
- ½ teaspoon of paprika
- 2 cloves garlic, minced
- 2 teaspoons reduced-sodium soy sauce (use wheat-free soy sauce if you are gluten sensitive)
- Water or low sodium vegetable broth to saute

Process

- Wash the potatoes and cut them into 1/2 inch (1 cm) cubes or pieces. Steam them with boiling water just until they are tender (around 15 minutes) when you perfume them with a fork. Rinse them with cold water, then drain and set aside.
- Rinse the green vegetables and then remove the thick stems. Chop off or tear the leaves into small pieces.
- Heat the water or broth in a large skillet and add the onion and garlic. Skip them until they are tender.
- Add the cooked potatoes, pepper, and paprika. Use a spatula to gently rotate the mixture and mix all the ingredients.
- Spread the green vegetables on top of the potato mixture. Spray them with soy sauce. Cover and cook, stirring occasionally, until tender.

67.Hot Beans

What you will need

- 1 pound green beans
- 8 cloves garlic finely chopped
- 2 tablespoons vinegar
- 2 tablespoons reduced-sodium soy sauce (use wheat-free soy sauce if you are gluten sensitive)

- ¼ teaspoon red pepper flakes
- Water or low sodium vegetable broth to saute

Process

- Rinse the beans, cut the ends, and break them into 1 inch (3 cm) pieces.
- Steam with boiling water until tender, 7 to 10 minutes.
- Heat the water or broth in a pan and sauté the garlic until it is tender. Add the vinegar, soy sauce, and red pepper flakes and then add the steamed beans.
- Cook for 1 minute and then transfer them to a serving plate.

68. Broccoli with mustard sauce

What you will need

- 1 bunch broccoli
- ¼ cup vinegar
- 1 teaspoon ground mustard with stone or Dijon mustard
- 1 clove of minced or ground garlic

Process

- Break broccoli into bite-sized corsages. Peel the woody stem and slice the softer stem into thin slices of ½ inch (1 cm).
- Steam until soft, about 5 minutes. Meanwhile, beat the dressing ingredients in a serving bowl.
- Add the broccoli to the steam and mix.
- Serve immediately.

69.Toasted Cobs

What you will need

- 1 to 2 ears per person, keeping the leaves
- Salt to taste (optional)
- Lemon slices
- chili powder

Process

- Soak the cob (keeping the leaves) in water for 20 minutes or more.
- Place the cob on the grill in a single layer at medium to low temperature for 8 to 12 minutes.
- The leaves will be charred while the corn is steamed inside them. Lower or start them before serving.
- Serve with salt (optional), lemon slices, and chili powder to season.

70.Steamed green vegetables

What you will need

- 1 large bunch of green vegetables: chard, kale, brown mustard, etc.
- ½ teaspoon umeboshi vinegar or vinegar of your choice

Process

- Cut or tear green vegetables into large bite-sized pieces.
- Let the water boil before adding the vegetables, to ensure rapid and complete vaporization.
- Let it evaporate for 5 minutes and add vinegar, mix and serve.

71.Garlic Spinach

What you will need

- 1 large bunch of fresh spinach
- 3 cloves of garlic

- 1 teaspoon vinegar
- Water or low sodium vegetable broth to saute

Process

- Wash the spinach.
- Peel and chop the garlic.
- Sauté the garlic in water or vegetable broth over medium heat until it softens.
- Add the spinach to the hot pan. Use the tongs to turn the spinach until all are barely withered.
- Sprinkle with vinegar and black pepper and serve.

72.sweet potatoes!

What you will need

- 2 to 3 yams or sweet potatoes (red yams make a very colorful dish)
- 2 to 3 apples
- 1 tablespoon of jam or spreadable fruit (100% fruit, no added sugar, peach, orange or pineapple)
- ½ cup of orange juice

Process

- Preheat the oven to 300-350 ° F (177 ° C).
- Peel and thinly slice sweet potatoes and apples.

- Combine spreadable fruit and orange juice.
- Place sweet potatoes and apples on a baking sheet.
- Pour the orange mixture over the sweet potatoes and apples and cover with a lid or aluminum.
- Bake for 45 minutes at 350 ° F (177 ° C).
- Sweet potatoes will be ready when they are easily pierced with a fork.

73. Garlic mashed potatoes

What you will need

- 8 medium red potatoes
- ½ teaspoon black pepper
- 10 to 12 cloves of fresh garlic
- 1 to 2 cups of potato water
- 1 cup non-dairy milk without sugar
- Water or low sodium vegetable broth to saute
- Salt or pepper to taste (optional)

Process

- Cut the potatoes into eighths (leave the peels).
- Cover with water and let them boil over medium heat until soft, about 15 minutes.
- Peel, crush and chop the garlic cloves.

- Sauté the garlic in a small saucepan with water or vegetable broth until it softens. Set it aside.
- Drain cooked potatoes over a bowl to collect your water.
- Using a manual crusher or electric mixer, crush the potatoes. Add a cup of the water from the potatoes and add the salt, pepper, and sauteed garlic.
- Add more water from the potatoes or milk, as necessary, to obtain a creamy consistency.
- Serve the mash immediately or keep it in the hot oven covered until ready to eat.

74.Stuffed baked potatoes

Stuffed potatoes usually depend on butter, sour cream, bacon, or cheese. Without saturated fats, these potatoes are simple, satisfying, and completely delicious.

What you will need

- 2 Russet or Yukon potatoes (yellow potatoes), each approximately 8 ounces (227 g)
- 1/3 cup milk without milk, simple, without sweetener
- 4 tablespoons hummus, oil-free

- 1 cup cooked and chopped vegetables (onions, broccoli, cauliflower, etc.)
- ½ teaspoon hot sauce
- ½ teaspoon kosher salt (optional)

Process

- Preheat the oven to 300-375 ° F (190 ° C). Prepare the potatoes for baking by washing them well and inserting a fork or knife several times so that the smoke escapes during the baking process.
- Bake for about an hour, or until tender when inserting a fork. Remove them from the oven and allow them to rest until they cool enough to touch them. Cut the potatoes lengthwise.
- Remove the inside of the potatoes with a spoon and place them in a bowl and be careful not to break the peels. Leave a small edge of the potato intact for support.
- Leave the prepared potato peels on a baking sheet.
- Mix the inside of the potatoes in a bowl, along with the remaining ingredients, and combine them completely. Pour the mixture back to the potato peels evenly until each half is round and almost overflowing. Place them back in the oven and bake until hot, about 15 minutes. Remove from oven and serve immediately.

What you will need

- 1 chopped onion
- 5 or 6 cups cooked brown rice
- 2 teaspoons curry powder
- 1 package of 16 ounces (454 g) of frozen peas and carrots, steamed and drained
- Salt (optional) and pepper to taste
- ¼ cup raisins, ground
- ¼ cup raw, filleted and toasted almonds

Process

- Sauté the sliced onion in a nonstick skillet dry until golden brown. Add a little water if necessary to prevent the onion from sticking to the pan.
- Add cooked brown rice, curry powder, steamed peas and carrots to the golden onion. Combine them well.
- Season generously with salt (optional) and pepper. Mix the curry rice combination with raisins and almonds and serve immediately.

What you will need

- 3 pounds of potatoes, a mixture of red and yellow (Yukon Gold)
- ½ handful of parsley
- ¼ cup nutritional yeast
- ½ teaspoon black pepper
- 2 cups of natural almond milk
- ½ tablespoon onion powder
- 1 teaspoon granulated garlic

Process

- Wash and cut the potatoes into large pieces, about the same size. Put them in a large pot and cover with water and let them boil until tender, 7 to 10 minutes. Meanwhile, wash and cut the parsley.
- Check the potatoes with a knife; It should slide between them when they are ready. Drain them. Enjoy the facial steam.
- Place the potatoes again in the hot pot. Let them steam, so they release some of the liquid. Add the remaining ingredients: parsley, almond milk, nutritional yeast, salt, pepper, onion powder, granulated garlic. Use a potato press to crush

everything together. Try the mash to adjust the seasoning.

77.Wild Rice Pilaf

What you will need

- ¾ cup wild rice pilaf mix
- 1 small carrot
- 2 celery stalks
- 1 bay leaf
- ½ teaspoon dried thyme
- 1 ½ cups of vegetable stock or water

Process

- Peel the carrot and cut the celery. Cut them into small cube-shaped pieces, the size of a bite.
- Rinse the rice in water to remove any dirt. In a small pot combine rice, carrot, celery, bay leaf, thyme, and vegetable broth. Cover it and let it boil. Reduce to a simmer. Cook for about 20 to 25 minutes, until the rice is tender.
- Remove the lid, stir the rice, and let it stand for a few minutes.

78. Vegan breakfast sausages with apples and shiitakes

What you will need

- 3 tablespoons ground chia seeds + 6 tablespoons water
- 2 cups of soy curls
- ½ cup shiitake mushrooms
- ½ cup of apples finally cut
- 1 can of 15 ounces (425 grams) of navy white beans or any other white beans
- 2 tablespoons maple syrup
- ½ teaspoon of natural maple flavoring
- 1 teaspoon ground sage
- 1 teaspoon fennel seeds (I crush them a little in a seed grinder for more flavor)
- 2 teaspoons onion powder
- 1 tablespoon tamari
- ½ teaspoon red chili flakes

Process

- Cover the soy curls with fresh water and let them soak for 10 minutes.
- Mix the chia with the water and set it aside.
- Line the baking sheet with parchment paper.
- Preheat the oven to 300-350 ° F (177 ° C).

- Remove the mushroom stems (save them for broth), cut the mushrooms into large pieces, and skip them in water until they are tender, and most of the water has evaporated.
- Drain the onion curls and squeeze as much water as you can.
- Drain and rinse the beans.
- Add the remaining mushrooms and ingredients, except apples, to a food processor and press until combined but still retain a thick consistency.
- Add the apples.
- Shape the mixture into logs, each 3 inches (8 cm) long and 1 inch (3 cm) in diameter.
- Place them on the baking sheet and bake for 30 minutes, turning once or twice to make sure they have a uniform color and heat distribution. Be careful! The sausages will be very fragile until they are cooked.

79.Caramelized and smoked Brussels sprouts

What you will need

- 1 small red onion
- 1 teaspoon of paprika smoked
- 1½ pounds (680 g) Brussels sprouts

- Salt and pepper

Process

- Preheat a wide skillet over high heat. If possible, use a cast-iron skillet.
- Peel, cut in half, and then thinly slice the red onion.
- Once your pan is incredibly hot, add the red onion in a single layer. Add smoked paprika on top.
- Leave the onions alone and let them brown for about 5 minutes.
- Meanwhile, cut the bottom of Brussels sprouts and then cut them in half. Allow the outer leaves to fall and discard them (they are often bitter). Wash split cabbages in half to remove any dirt.
- Once the onions begin to brown, stir and continue cooking until they are well browned, for another 5 minutes or so.
- Move the onions to the side of the pan.
- Add the Brussels sprouts cut in half to the pan and spread them so that they form a single layer as much as you can. Allow the cabbage to carbonize for a couple of minutes before stirring.
- When the cabbages are golden on one side, stir and continue cooking until they all have a little color. Stir frequently to prevent burning.
- After about 5 minutes, add 1 cup of water to the sprouts. The steam must finish cooking. If they are

larger, however, they may take longer, so add more water to prevent burning.

- Season with salt and pepper and serve.

80.Sweet potato and pineapple casserole with pecan streusel

This is a traditional southern festivities classic recipe. Sweet potatoes are roasted in it to a substantial and creamy perfection, crushed with pineapple and overlaid with gluten-free pecan streusel and oil covering.

What you will need

- 4 medium sweet potatoes (approximately 4 pounds or 2 kilos)
- 2 cups diced pineapple and juice (fresh, frozen or canned)
- 2 teaspoons ground cinnamon
- 1 teaspoon ground ginger
- 1 teaspoon grated nutmeg
- ¼ teaspoon salt (optional)
- ½ cup chopped dates or dates
- ½ cup brown rice flour
- ¼ cup pecan pieces
- ¼ cup cashew butter
- A little salt (as needed)

Process

- Preheat the oven to 425 ° F (218 ° C).
- To roast sweet potatoes: Scrub and place on a baking sheet. Bake at 425 ° F (218 ° C) until completely tender, about 1 hour - 90 minutes, depending on their size. This time is enough to make your streusel cover and prepare the pineapple.
- To make streusel coverage: Chop dates. Combine them with brown rice flour, pecan pieces, cashew butter, and a pinch of salt. Use your hands to shred them together, just as you would with a traditional butter streusel topping. You want the streusel to stay together in pieces the size of a pea. If it is not sticky, add a tablespoon of water and mix well. Check again and add the water, 1 tablespoon at a time, until you get the pea-sized pieces. Set aside the mixture for later use.
- To make the casserole: Cut and divide your pineapple into cubes. You need about 2 cups of diced pineapple. Combine with cinnamon, ginger, nutmeg, and salt. Sweet potatoes will be ready when a knife can easily slide in and out of them. Remove them from the oven and let them cool. When sweet potatoes are cold enough to handle, just peel them. Combine sweet potato pulp with pineapple spice mixture. Machine them to the

desired smoothness. To make the mixture completely creamy, you better use a food processor.

- Spread the pineapple and sweet potato mixture on a 9-inch (23 cm) baking sheet. Sprinkle the pecan streusel on top of the mixture. Bake at 350 degrees F (177 ° C) for 8 to 10 minutes, until golden brown on top.

81.Cabbage with peanuts

What you will need

- ½ cup diced onion
- 4 cloves garlic, minced
- ⅛ teaspoon red pepper flakes (optional)
- 4 tablespoons vegetable stock, divided
- 4 cups chopped cabbage
- 2 tomatoes, diced
- 2 tablespoons natural peanut butter mixed with 1/4 cup vegetable stock
- ½ teaspoon lemon juice
- Salt to taste
- ½ cup ground peanuts
- Ripe bananas

Process

- In a medium saucepan, sauté the onions, garlic and red pepper in flakes (if you use it) in two tablespoons of vegetable stock over medium-high heat for 3 to 5 minutes, until the onions are browned.
- Add the remaining 2 tablespoons of vegetable stock, cabbage, and tomatoes. Cover and cook over medium heat for 3 to 5 minutes.
- Add the peanut butter mixture and lemon juice. Cook for 2 to 3 minutes.
- Season with salt and add ground peanuts.
- Serve the cabbage with peanuts over the Ripe Bananas.

82.Sauteed sweet potato and kale

What you will need

Sauteed

- 2 sweet potatoes, peeled and diced (4 cups)
- 2 tablespoons vegetable stock
- ¼ cup diced onions
- 1 bunch kale, chopped (6 to 7 cups)

Lemon And Mostaza Sauce

- ¼ cup lemon juice
- ¼ cup low sodium soy sauce
- 1 tablespoon of Dijon mustard
- 1 teaspoon dried dill
- 1 teaspoon cornstarch mixed with 2 tablespoons water

Process

- Place the potatoes in a saucepan and cover with water. Cook over medium-high heat, soft, but not hot, until the potatoes. Drain it.
- In a medium skillet, mix the vegetable stock, onion, and kale. Cover and cook for 3 to 5 minutes over medium-high heat until the kale softens.
- In the oven, add the potatoes.
- In a casserole, add all the sauce ingredients and cook over medium-high heat until the mixture thickens.
- Attach 6 tablespoons of sauce and whisk gently. Cook 2 to 3 minutes, if necessary, adding up to 2 more tablespoons of sauce.
- Serve warm.

What you will need

- 5 cups quinoa
- 10 cups of water
- 2 bunches of red radishes
- 1 large bunch of mint leaves, finely chopped (about ½ cup)
- 6 lemons, squeezed (about 1 cup)
- 1 teaspoon of sea salt
- 3 tablespoons umeboshi plum vinegar
- 6 tablespoons raw pine nuts
- 6 medium cucumber cucumbers, peeled and diced
- 1 ½ cluster of fresh, finely chopped parsley (approximately 3 cups packed loose)

Process

- Rinse and strain the quinoa. Add water Heat until it boils, reduces heat to low, cover, and cooks for 20 to 25 minutes. Let it cool.
- Prepare the radishes. Cut them finely in cubes, quickly hide them in boiling water and let them cool.
- Mix the mint, lemon juice, salt, and vinegar. Add this mixture to quinoa.

- Toast the pine nuts in a small skillet over low heat for a few minutes, stirring frequently.
- Add the boiled radishes, cucumbers, pine nuts, and parsley.

84.Sweet and spicy coriander and ginger salad

What you will need

- 1 large purple carrot, grated (about a cup)
- 2 medium tomatoes, diced (approximately one cup)
- 1 large yellow apple, peeled and diced
- 2 tablespoons lemon juice
- 1 large handful of fresh cilantro, chopped
- 1 green jalapeno pepper, chopped
- 1 teaspoon grated ginger
- 3 tablespoons hemp seed

Process

- Mix all the ingredients several times, until the flavors have combined.

85.Vegan muffins of rainbow chard and tofu

These vegan muffins contain a powerful nutritional force, unlike traditional muffins, which are often filled with butter, sugar, and saturated fat. They make a great breakfast and are the perfect size for a light lunch or a mid-afternoon snack.'

What you will need

Vegetable Filling

- Vegetable broth (to saute)
- 2 cloves garlic, minced
- ½ sweet potato (grated)
- 1 handful of spinach
- Rainbow chard (chopped)
- Parsley

For The Mass

- 1 cup oatmeal
- 1 cup of rice flour
- 1 teaspoon cornstarch
- 1 teaspoon baking powder
- 2 tablespoons flaxseed
- ½ teaspoon cumin
- 1 teaspoon salt
- 1 teaspoon nutmeg
- ½ cup of tofu
- 7 tablespoons oatmeal (or soft mixed tofu)
- 1 cup oat milk

Aderez

- 1 to 2 tablespoons hemp seeds

Process

- Preheat the oven to 400 ° F (204 ° C).
- Preheat a large skillet over medium heat. Pour a little vegetable stock and add the garlic and sweet potato. Saute for about 5 minutes, and then place the spinach. Cook for another 2 minutes until the spinach is completely soft. Remove from heat and let it cool completely before continuing to the next step.
- In a large bowl, mix all the dry ingredients. Crush the tofu well and add it to the dry ingredients.
- Add the chopped cooked vegetables, chard, and parsley in the large bowl and mix well until all the ingredients are combined.
- Fill the baking pans (I use baking paper for each muffin).
- Sprinkle hemp seeds on each muffin.
- Bake for 25 minutes.

86.Potato chips with salt and baked vinegar

What you will need

- 5 russet potatoes

- 2-3 cups apple cider vinegar
- 2 tablespoons nutritional yeast flakes
- Sea salt (optional)

Process

- Preheat the oven to 218 ° C (425 ° F). Line a sheet of parchment paper for baking.
- Peel or wash the potatoes and cut them into 1/4 inch (6 mm) thick slices lengthwise. Stack and cut some slices of potatoes in the shape of thin matches at a time.
- In a large pot, put the potatoes and pour in enough vinegar to cover them. Cook 10 minutes over medium-high heat. For more than 10 minutes, do not cook potatoes or they will become too soft and may not be crispy in the oven. Drain the potatoes, but do not rinse them in a colander.
- Place the potatoes on the prepared baking sheet in a single layer. Sprinkle with nutritional yeast and salt to taste (if you use it).
- Cook until golden brown for 30 minutes. Serve hot.

CHAPTER FIVE
Plant-based diet Snacks recipes

87.Red applesauce and beet

Ingredient

- 2 cups unpeeled apple, diced or grated
- 1 cup boneless cherries or mixed berries
- 1 cup unpeeled grated beets
- 1 tablespoon date paste
- ½ teaspoon cinnamon
- 2 tablespoons of water

Process

- Place all the ingredients in a saucepan.
- Take to a boil and cook until apples and beets have softened for 10-15 minutes.
- Crush with a potato masher or process in a food processor for a smoother consistency.
- Serve alone or use it to decorate Halloween treats.

88. Apple "Halloween" lamps

Adorable and easy to prepare, these apple and peanut butter lanterns are a delicious breakfast, snack, or snack for Halloween.

What you will need

- 6 red apples
- 1 cup peanut butter
- 1 tablespoon date paste
- ½ teaspoon of pumpkin pie spice
- 1 cup of oil-free granola

Process

- Preheat the oven to 300-350 ° F (177 ° C).
- Cut the top of each apple.
- Take out the inside with a spoon or a melon. Make sure the walls are thick.
- Carefully carve the face of the flashlight to make eyes and mouth.
- Melt peanut butter in a saucepan until smooth and smooth.
- In a bowl, combine melted peanut butter with date paste and pumpkin spices.
- Fill the apples with the peanut butter mixture and replace the apple tops.
- Bake the apples on a baking sheet for 10 minutes.

- Place the granola in the apples and bake for another 10 minutes.
- Serve immediately.

89. Frankenstein Avocado Toast

Traditionally, Halloween festivities begin with the sunset, but mashing some avocado for this monstrous, fun, and easy breakfast will definitely elevate your mood. Best of all, the combination of complex carbohydrates and healthy fats will supply you with the fuel needed for a spooky day of costume contests, clothing, and decorations at work or school!

What you will need

- 4 slices of whole wheat bread
- 1 avocado, cut in half and seeded
- 1 tablespoon lemon juice
- ½ teaspoon garlic powder
- A pinch of sea salt

DECORATIVE INGREDIENTS

- 1 nori leaf or a dark lettuce leaf
- Black beans
- Sliced red pepper
- Mexicrema dressing

Process

- bread in a toaster or in a toaster oven.
- While the bread is toasted, place the avocado in a bowl.
- Add the lemon juice, garlic powder and salt, and pestle with a fork or potato masher.
- Trim the nori leaf or dark lettuce to form the hair.
- Decorate the Franken toast forming the hair with the nori or the lettuce, the eyes with the black beans, the mouth with the sliced pepper, and the frame of the face with the dressing.

90. Almond butter toast with sweet potatoes and blueberries

What you will need

- 1 sweet potato, sliced half a centimeter thick
- ¼ cup almond butter
- ½ cup blueberries

Process

- Preheat the oven to 350-360 ° F (177 ° C).
- Place the sweet potato slices on baking paper. Bake until soft, approximately 20 minutes. (You can also

cook them in a toaster, but you would need to activate it at high temperature for three or four cycles).

- Serve hot, coat with peanut butter and cranberries. Store any leftover sweet potato slices, without dressings, in an airtight container inside the refrigerator for a week. Reheat them in a toaster or in a toaster oven and cover them as instructed.

91.Chile with "cheese" and sauce

This rich and creamy non-dairy "cheese" spread is so spectacularly delicious that you will be doing it over and over again. The striking flavors combine beautifully with the sauce. Together they can be served as a side dish of raw vegetables or oil-free baked tortillas for a healthy snack, which will satisfy the public.

What you will need

"CHEESE" UNTABLE

- 1 cup raw cashews
- 2 red peppers, roasted, with the peel and seeds removed
- ¼ cup fresh lemon juice
- 3 tablespoons nutritional yeast
- 1 teaspoon salt

- ½ teaspoon red pepper in crushed flakes, or to taste

SAUCE

- 1 ½ cups diced tomato
- ½ cup diced bell pepper
- ¼ finely sliced red onion
- ½ teaspoon grated garlic
- 1 tablespoon fresh lemon juice
- 1 tablespoon chopped fresh cilantro
- 1 teaspoon jalapeño, seeded and chopped
- Salt and fresh ground pepper

Process

"CHEESE" UNTABLE

- In a high power blender, mix all ingredients with 2 tablespoons of water and process everything until smooth.

SAUCE

- In a medium bowl, combine all the ingredients on the list until jalapeño. Season everything with salt and pepper to taste.

92. Zucchini rainbow rolls

This is a simple and complete snack that is easy to eat along the way, but it is also perfect as a party snack.

What you will need

- 1 zucchini
- 2 teaspoons hummus
- ¼ cup sprouts of clover, alfalfa, mung beans or sunflower
- 3 ounces (85 grams) of the firm or extra-firm tofu, sliced
- ¼ cup slices of multicolored pepper (red, yellow, orange or green)
- 3 or 4 mushrooms, sliced
- ⅛ to ¼ teaspoon ground cumin
- ⅛ to ¼ teaspoon cayenne pepper
- 1 tablespoon nutritional yeast flakes

Process

- Cut the zucchini lengthwise into long thin slices with a mandolin or a sharp knife.
- Lay the hummus on the slices of zucchini.
- Place some sprouts and slices of tofu, pepper, and mushrooms on one end of each zucchini slice.
- Sprinkle with cumin, cayenne, and nutritional yeast.

What you will need

- 2 slices of bread
- 1 avocado, sliced
- ½ lemon juice
- 2 tablespoons pumpkin seeds
- 1 pinch red pepper flakes
- 1 pinch smoked paprika
- 1 pinch of sesame seeds
- 1 pinch of salt
- 1 pinch of black pepper

Process

- Toast the bread.
- Place the avocado slices on the toast.
- Sprinkle the lemon juice over the avocado.
- Sprinkle pumpkin seeds, red pepper flakes, sesame seeds, salt and black pepper on top, to taste.

94.Pumpkin and oatmeal bars

What you will need

- 3 cups thick oatmeal

- 1 cup seedless dates
- ½ cup of boiling water
- 2 teaspoons pumpkin pie spice
- 1 tablespoon ground flaxseed or chia seeds
- ¼ cup small sliced nuts (optional)
- ¼ cup of vegetable milk
- 1 cup mashed pumpkin

Process

- Preheat the oven to 350 degrees F.
- Chop the dates into small pieces, place them in a bowl, and pour the hot water over them. Let stand for 10 minutes.
- Add the dry ingredients to a bowl and mix well.
- Add dates with water, squash, and vegetable milk to dry ingredients, and mix well.
- Cover a square baking sheet with baking paper, then firmly press the mixture into the pan.
- Bake for 15-20 minutes.
- Let the mixture cool completely in the container before cutting it into 16 squares or 8 large bars.
- Store in the refrigerator for up to 7 days.

95.Oatmeal and Apple Cookies

These very healthy cookies are simple and delicious - you use only 5 ingredients and need only 5 minutes to put them together!

What you will need

- 2 cups gluten-free oatmeal
- 2 cups applesauce
- ½ cup raisins
- 1½ tablespoons chia seeds
- 2 teaspoons cinnamon

Process

- Preheat to 350 ° F (177 ° C) in the oven.
- In a medium bowl, put all 5 ingredients and stir until combined. Let stand during the heating of the oven for 10 minutes.
- Serve big spoonfuls of the mixture (covered in baking paper) on the cookie sheet. Gently flatten and spread the mixture to the size and shape you want with the back of the spoon. Bake for about 25 minutes.
- After removal from the oven, move the cookies to the rack to cool.
- Don't try to eat them once!

96.Homemade granola

What you will need

- 3 cups flaked oatmeal
- ¼ cup chopped raw nuts
- ¼ cup raw pecans, chopped
- ¼ cup raw almonds, chopped
- ½ cup pure maple syrup
- 2 teaspoons vanilla
- 2 teaspoons cinnamon
- 1 pinch of salt (optional)

Process

- Preheat the oven to 250-300 ° F (149 ° C).
- Combine all ingredients in a bowl, mixing well to cover everything with maple syrup. Spread the mixture on a baking sheet or broiler pan.
- Bake until the mixture browns, stirring occasionally, 30 to 40 minutes. Transfer the baking sheet to a wire rack and let it cool completely. Keep the granola refrigerated in an airtight jar.

97.Heart-shaped oatmeal and banana cookies

What you will need

INGREDIENTS OF COOKIES

- 2 large ripe bananas
- 2 cups of flaked oatmeal
- 2 tablespoons peanut butter
- 1 pinch of sea salt
- 2 teaspoons cocoa powder (to add later)

INGREDIENTS OF THE CREAM OF MARAÑONES

- ½ cup soaked cashews
- ½ banana
- 1 teaspoon vanilla extract
- 1 pinch of sea salt
- Juice of half a small lemon
- Enough water or dairy-free milk to make the creamy smooth, but not too liquid

INGREDIENTS OF DATES AND CHOCOLATE

- 1 cup dates
- ¾ cup of water
- 3 tablespoons cocoa powder (or half cocoa + half carob)
- 1 pinch of sea salt

Process

PREPARATION OF COOKIES

- Puree with bananas and peanut butter with sea salt in a blender.
- In a bowl, mix the peanut and banana puree with the oatmeal in flakes.
- Heat the oven to 350 ° F (177 ° C).
- Line a baking sheet with parchment paper. Take the heart-shaped cookie cutter (or in any way you like) and place it on the baking sheet.
- Take about 1.2 ounces (35 g) of cookie dough and press it evenly on the cookie cutter. Remove the cutter with the spoon. Repeat until you have 8 cookies on the tray.
- Add 2 teaspoons of raw cocoa powder to the remaining dough. Also, add a few splashes of dairy-free milk to mix.
- Repeat step 5 until the dough disappears.
- Bake the cookies on the grill in the middle of the oven for 16 minutes and let them cool.

PREPARATION OF THE CREAM OF MARAÑONES

- Soak the cashews for at least 2 hours. Drain and rinse them.
- Combine all the ingredients in a blender (as it is a very small portion, I used a chopper) and mix them until a thick cream forms. You will need a spoon to help you. Add the liquid gradually and only as much as necessary to combine all the ingredients well.

- Transfer the cream to a bowl and set it aside.

PREPARATION OF DATES AND CHOCOLATE

- Cut the dates into smaller pieces and let them soak in ¾ cup of water for at least 30 minutes.
- Mix dates, soaking water, salt, and cocoa, until a lump-free cream is left. You will have to pick them up with a spoon between each mixture.
- Decorate the cookies as you want. You can also use melted dark chocolate as I did.

98.Coconut snacks

These mango and coconut balls are a plant-based pleasure that will melt in your mouth. This dessert has no added sugar and does not contain oil.

What you will need

- 1 cup pineapple juice
- 2 cups diced mango
- 2 ripe bananas, diced
- ½ vanilla branch
- 4 cups shredded coconut
- ¾ cup roasted grated coconut

Process

- In a small pot, cook pineapple juice, mango, bananas, and vanilla over medium-low heat for 5 minutes.
- Scrape the seeds of the vanilla branch in the pot and discard the branch; then cook them for two more minutes.
- Put the ingredients that are in the pot and the 4 cups of grated coconut inside a food processor with an "S" shaped leaf and process them until you get a mixture without lumps, but firm.
- Let the mixture cool for about 1 to 2 hours, then, using a small scoop for ice cream or a spoon, place a small amount in your hands and make a ball before rolling it over the toasted coconut.
- Repeat the process until all your coconut snacks are rolled, I bet you can't eat just one!

99.Cucumber and kale open sandwich

What you will need

- 2 slices of whole-grain bread, toasted
- 2 to 3 tablespoons of hummus prepared without tahini or oil
- 1 chopped green onion
- ¼ cup chopped fresh cilantro

- 2 medium kale leaves, chopped into small bite-sized pieces (about the size of coriander leaves)
- ½ small cucumber
- Mustard of your choice
- Lemon pepper (Mrs. Dash and Frontier brands have no salt)

Process

- Spread hummus generously on toasted bread. Sprinkle the green onion, cilantro, and kale evenly over the hummus.
- Slice the cucumber in 8 circles and spread each with a thin layer of mustard.
- Place the cucumber slices, with the mustard down, on top of the coriander and kale layer and press down, if necessary, so that they remain in place.
- Sprinkle the open sandwich generously with lemon pepper, cut it in half or quarters, if desired, and serve.

100.   Delicious minisandías

What you will need

- 2 tender cucumbers
- 1 piece of watermelon heart, preferably dense and bright with a minimum of seeds removed
- 1 pinch of black sesame seeds (toasted)

Process

- Start by cutting the ends of the cucumbers and then cut a 2 "(5 cm) piece of each end.
- Set the center section aside for another use (salads, etc.).
- Place each semicircular piece on its end and use the small tip of a Parisian spoon to take half a sphere from each.
- Use the same technique to carve identical pieces of the heart of the watermelon and place them inside the cucumber, with the flat side up.
- If the pieces are not kept flush, you can carefully cut the excess with a peeling knife.
- Finish by pressing the black sesame seeds with a wet finger and use it to spread them on the surface of the melon.

101.   Roasted Chickpeas

What you will need

- 2 cans of 15 ounces (425 g) of chickpeas, rinsed and drained
- 1 teaspoon garlic powder
- 2 teaspoons chili powder
- ½ teaspoon of sea salt
- 2 tablespoons lemon juice

Process

- Preheat the oven to 400 ° F (200 ° C). Line a baking sheet with parchment paper and set it aside.
- Place the chickpeas in a one-gallon (liter) sealed plastic bag and add seasonings. Shake well until completely covered.
- Spread spicy chickpeas evenly over the prepared baking sheet.
- Bake for 45 to 55 minutes, stirring every 15 to 20 minutes so that the chickpeas cook evenly, until golden brown.
- Serve hot or cold for a snack at any time.

CHAPTER SIX
Plant-based diet Soup recipes

102. Nopal Soup

The cactus is famous for its health benefits. Not only is it delicious, but it is also rich in antioxidants, fiber, vitamins, and minerals. It tastes similar to green beans (tender beans) or okra. The cactus is also known as the Mexican-born prickly pear cactus. Since the Aztecs in various pre-Hispanic dishes, nopales have been eaten as vegetables. Cooked or raw, they can be eaten and used in a variety of dishes such as soups, stews, tacos, and salads.

What you will need

- 2 pounds of nopales, clean and diced
- 4 Roma tomatoes
- ¼ white onion
- 2 cloves of garlic
- 1 chipotle chili in adobo (optional)
- 3 cups of vegetable stock
- 1 tablespoon dried oregano
- Salt and pepper to taste

OPTIONAL COVERAGES

- Avocado
- Coriander

- Chives
- Lemon or Lime Juice

Process

- Cook the nopales for 20-25 minutes in boiling water with salt or until they lose their bright color and are tender to bit.
- Place the tomatoes, onion, garlic, and chipotle in a blender glass. Blend until you get a creamy consistency.
- Remove the nopales from the heat, drain them, and rinse them with enough cold water. Leave aside.
- In a pot, sauté the tomato sauce for about 3 minutes.
- Add cooked nopales and oregano to tomato broth. Let cook another 15 minutes.
- add salt and pepper to taste.
- Serve on soup plates and add toppings.

103.   Matzo Ball Soup

What you will need

MATZO BALLS

- 1 ½ cups quinoa flakes

- 1 ½ cups of mixture gluten purpose flour
- 2 teaspoons onion powder
- 1 teaspoon garlic powder
- ¼ teaspoon of sea salt
- 2 cups of boiling water
- 6 tablespoons pumpkin puree

SOUP

- 1 medium yellow onion, chopped
- ¼ cup of Coconut Aminos
- ½ teaspoon freshly ground black pepper
- 5 medium carrots, peeled and sliced
- 3 celery stalks, diced
- 2 parsnips, peeled and sliced
- 1 cup fresh parsley, chopped
- 8 cups of vegetable broth without sodium

COVER

- 3 tablespoons fresh dill, finely chopped

Process

- Preheat the oven to 200-300 degrees F (148 ° C). Cover a 15 x 13 inch (38 x 33 cm) baking sheet with parchment paper.

- To make matzo balls: Beat quinoa flakes, flour, onion powder, garlic powder, and salt in a medium bowl. Add the boiling water and the pumpkin and stir to combine.
- Take at least a tablespoon of the mixture and form a ball. Place the ball on the prepared baking sheet. Repeat until you have used the entire mixture. You should have approximately 30 balls.
- Bake the matzo balls until they are a light golden color, approximately 20 minutes. Turn the balls halfway through cooking.
- Transfer the baking sheet from the oven to a wire rack and let it stand for 10 minutes.
- To make the soup: heat the onion in a large pot over medium heat and stir until it begins to release its aroma, approximately for a minute.
- Add the Coconut Aminos, black pepper, carrots, celery, parsnips, and parsley and cook, stirring occasionally, until the vegetables release their aroma and are slightly soft, about two minutes. Add the broth and boil.
- Reduce the heat intensity, cover the pot, and let simmer for about 35 minutes.
- Serve immediately and place several matzo balls in each bowl of soup. Sprinkle dill in the soup.
- the soup tastes even better the next day, and even better two days later.

What you will need

- 2 yellow onions, sliced
- 3 cloves garlic, minced
- 6 carrots, peeled and sliced
- 4 celery stalks, sliced
- 5 sprigs of dill
- 4 sprigs of parsley
- 4 scallions
- 10 cups of water

Process

- Add the onions over medium heat to a large pot and stir until the scent is released, about a minute. Add the garlic, carrots, celery, dill, parsley, and scallions and cook for about a minute until the herbs release their fragrance.
- Add the water and allow it to boil. Low the heat, cover the pot and cook for 45 minutes.
- Turn off the heat and allow about 15 minutes to cool the broth.

- Filter the broth through a sieve and freeze it into ice buckets, or pour it into glass jars if you use it immediately. It's going to stay a week or so.

105.   Comforting noodle and chickpea soup

What you will need

- 1 cup onion, diced
- 2 carrots, sliced
- 1 celery stalk, diced (optional)
- 2 medium diced potatoes
- 3 cloves garlic, minced
- ½ teaspoon dried thyme
- 4 cups of vegetable stock
- 2 cups of water
- ¼ cup chicken seasoning
- 6 ounces cooked spaghetti (noodles)
- 2 cups cooked chickpeas
- Salt and pepper to taste
- fresh cilantro chopped to taste

CONDIMENTO FOR "CHICKEN" (PREPARE 1 ¾ CUP)

- 1 ⅓ cup nutritional yeast

- 3 tablespoons onion powder
- 1 tablespoon garlic powder
- 1½ tablespoon dried basil
- 1 teaspoon oregano
- ½ teaspoon of turmeric
- 2 teaspoons sea salt

Process

- Sauté the onion in a medium saucepan over medium heat until it begins to soften, about 3 minutes.
- Add the carrots, potatoes, and celery (if you are using it) and sauté for 2-3 minutes.
- Add garlic, thyme, "chicken seasoning," vegetable stock, and water.
- Cook over medium-low heat until all vegetables are tender, about 20 minutes.
- Add the chickpeas and pasta.
- Season with salt and pepper to taste.
- Serve with some fresh cilantro on top.

106.   Soup loaded with miso noodles.

What you will need

- 4 servings of buckwheat noodles or brown rice noodles, uncooked
- 3 cups of vegetable stock
- 3 cups of water
- 1 cup of carrot cut into julienne
- 1 cup julienne zucchini
- 1 cup thinly sliced shiitake mushrooms
- 1 cup broccoli corsages
- 3 tablespoons miso paste
- 1 package of firm tofu (14 ounces or 396 grams), cut into one-inch cubes (2.5 centimeters)
- ¼ cup chopped green onion
- 1 sheet of roasted nori seaweed, cut into pieces

Process

- Prepare the noodles as per the instructions for the box. Set them apart.
- Cook the vegetable stock and water in a medium saucepan over high heat. Remove the carrots, courgettes, mushrooms, and broccoli, add heat, and cook for five minutes.
- Use a ladle to pass to a small bowl a cup of broth. Use a fork in the broth to dissolve the miso paste and return it to the pot. Add tofu, green onions, and cooked noodles and cook for another minute until warm.
- Move to bowls and cover with seaweed nori.

107. Bone" mineral broth and vegetables

This vegan mineral broth is a beautiful snack, which will also provide you with many nutrients. It is not necessary to use animal bones to create this healthy recipe.

What you will need

- 2 strips of 5 inches (12.7 centimeters) of dried Kombu seaweed
- 6 mushroom shiitake dry
- 6 carrots cut into pieces
- 2 medium onions cut into pieces
- 1 leek, with white and green parts, cut into pieces
- small bunch of celery, including the heart, cut into pieces
- 5 cloves of unpeeled garlic, cut in half
- 1 normal or small winter squash with peel, seeded and cut into pieces
- 1 piece of fresh ginger 5 inches (12.7 centimeters), sliced
- 4 cups chopped vegetables, such as kale or chard
- ½ bunch fresh parsley
- 1 package of 40 g (1.4 oz) dried daikon radish (optional)

Process

- Combine all ingredients in a broth or large soup pot.
- Fill the pot 2 inches (5 centimeters) below the edge with water, cover it and let it boil.
- Remove the lid, reduce the temperature to medium / low, and let it boil for a minimum of two hours.
- As the broth heats up, some of the water will evaporate; add more if the vegetables are exposed.
- Cook over low heat until you can taste the delicacy of vegetables. Strain the broth and pour it into glass jars. Refrigeration works well with any broth.

108.   Noodle soup with broccoli and ginger

What you will need

- 3 medium broccoli heads (7 to 8 cups)
- 1 package of small rice noodles (12 ounces or 340 g)
- 16 ounces (453 g) firm tofu, cut into ¼ to ½ inch (6 to 12 mm) cubes
- 2 pieces of two inches (5 cm) of wakame or alaria seaweed
- 4 quarts (4 liters) of water
- ¾ cup wheat-free or regular tamari
- 2 medium onions, diced (approximately 2½ cups)

- 4 tablespoons fresh ginger root, chopped or finely grated
- 3 tablespoons mirin (rice wine for cooking)
- 6 medium carrots, diced (approximately 3 cups)
- 4 medium parsnips, diced (approximately 2 cups)

Process

- Separate the broccoli stems from their heads. Remove the hard outer layer of the stems and cut them into small bite-sized pieces. Set them aside.
- Separate broccoli headed into small pieces and set aside.
- Cook the noodles, strain them and let them cool. Set them aside.
- Sauté the tofu in a nonstick skillet for 3 to 4 minutes. Add 4 teaspoons of tamari and sauté for another 3 to 4 minutes. Set it aside.
- Place the wakame or alaria seaweed in 4 liters of water and bring it to a boil.
- Lower the heat to medium, add the onions and cook for 10 minutes.
- Remove the vegetables from the sea, cut them into small pieces, and return them to the pot.
- Add the ginger, the remaining tamari, and the peeper.
- Continue cooking over medium heat for 5 minutes.

- Add carrots, parsnips, and broccoli stems. Cook for 2 minutes.
- Gently stir the noodles and sauteed tofu. Cook for 1 minute.
- Add the broccoli heads. Cook over low heat until the broccoli is tender, for about 2 or 3 minutes.

109.   Chilled

What you will need

- 6-8 corn tortillas
- Mashed potatoes, enough to fill the tortillas
- 2 cans of pinto beans, low sodium
- 1 fat onion slice
- 1 teaspoon dried oregano
- ½ - 1 cup of water or vegetable stock
- Salt and pepper to taste

Decor

- sauce
- Chopped lettuce
- Herbal sour cream

Process

- Preheat the oven to 325 degrees F (163 degrees C).
- Put the pinto beans, onion slice, oregano, and ½ cup of water in a blender. Process until you get a creamy consistency but you can easily spill it on the tortillas.

Add the other half of water little by little until you get the desired consistency.

- To make the rolls with the tortillas, heat them in the microwave for 30 seconds or until they are flexible when folding.
- Place an omelet on a flat surface and place 1 or 2 tablespoons of mashed potatoes in the middle of the tortilla. Carefully roll the tortilla. Place the rolls in a baking dish. Make sure the tortilla overlay fold is placed down.
- Bathe the rolls with enough bean sauce until completely covered.
- Bake for 20 minutes or until hot.
- Garnish with lettuce, salsa, and sour cream.
- Serve hot.

110.   Black Bean and Quinoa Burgers

Smoked and meatless, these fantastic and easy black bean burgers are great on a bread roll with your favorite companions.

What you will need

- 3 cups cooked black beans
- 1 cup cooked quinoa
- 1 cup flaked oatmeal
- 2 tablespoons ground flaxseed

- ½ cup barbecue sauce
- ½ teaspoon of liquid smoke or smoked paprika
- 1 teaspoon garlic powder
- ½ teaspoon onion powder

Additional barbecue sauce for hamburger

Process

- Preheat the oven to 400F.
- Partially pest the beans.
- include the rest of the ingredients and mix well.
- Shape the burgers with your hands compacting well.
- Put the burgers on a baking sheet covered with baking paper.
- Bake the hamburgers for 15 minutes.
- Flip the burgers and cover with a layer of barbecue sauce.
- Bake for 10-15 more minutes.

111.   Roasted Cauliflower with Turmeric

Golden brown and aromatic, this tasty roasted cauliflower is unforgettable.

What you will need

- 1 large cauliflower
- 2 teaspoons finely grated fresh ginger

- 1 tablespoon tahini
- 1 tablespoon organic miso paste, non-GMO
- 3 tablespoons vegetable stock
- 3 prunes or dates, chopped
- ½ teaspoon of turmeric powder
- 2 tablespoons tamari
- Ground black pepper, to taste
- Black and white sesame seeds, to decorate
- Sliced green onion, to decorate (optional)

Process

- Preheat the oven to 425 degrees F.
- Cut the leaves and stem at the bottom of the head of the cauliflower, so that it is flat.
- Click with a sharp blade so that the spices penetrate the cauliflower.
- Remove the cauliflower from the oven and sprinkle the top with one of the green onions (optional), the tamari, a pinch of ground black pepper, and sesame seeds before serving.
- Mix the ginger, tahini, miso paste, broth, prums or dates, and turmeric in a food processor.
- Rub the paste over the cauliflower using your hands, ensuring that it is spread everywhere, even at the edges.

- In the oven, roast the cauliflower for 45 minutes or until golden is soft and cool.

112. Creamy mushroom lasagna, gluten-free

What you will need

- 3 cloves garlic, ground
- 16 ounces of chopped champignons (you can use a mixture of different champignons)
- 1 tablespoon of tamari or aminos (amino acids in liquid, in Spanish) of coconut or soy sauce, gluten-free
- 1 teaspoon dried thyme
- Thirty-four cup raw cashews, soaked for a few hours, drained overnight.
- 1 cup vegetable broth + a little more to saute garlic and mushrooms
- 2 large handfuls of spinach
- 10 ounces of lasagna sheets, gluten-free (I love Tinkyada brown rice pasta)
- 4 cups marinara sauce, purchased at the store (a 32 oz or 946 ml bottle) or homemade
- Nutritional Yeast (optional)

Process

- In a skillet, heat a little vegetable stock at medium temperature. When it is hot, add the garlic and skip it until it releases the aroma. This will take a minute. Add the mushrooms, tamari (or coconut or soy amino sauce, gluten-free), and thyme. Cook, mix more or less every minute, for six or eight minutes or until the mushrooms release their water, and a small broth begins to form.
- Combine cashews and vegetable broth in a high-speed blender and blend until the mixture is completely uniform. This may take five minutes, depending on your blender's speed and power. Verse the cashew sauce with the mushrooms in the pan. Reduce heat to medium-low and simmer to let the sauce thicken, stirring frequently.
- make the lasagna sheets according to the package instructions. Be sure to do this after your mushroom sauce is ready so that the slices do not remain static for a long time and begin to stick. Spread a third of the marinara sauce in the bottom of a baking sheet eight to eleven inches in size (20 to 28 cm). Add a layer of sheets. Cover them with half the mushroom cream. Add a layer of sheets. Use another third of the marinara sauce to cover them. Add the remaining mushroom cream. Add the last layer of sheets and cover them with the remaining marinara sauce.

- Cover the lasagna with foil and bake for 30 minutes. Remove the paper, add some nutritional yeast on top, if you want, and cook it for another 15 minutes. Let the lasagna stand for five minutes before serving.

113.   Spaghetti and Meatballs

Use this meatball master recipe to prepare a variety of dishes, from Swedish meatballs to barbecue-style meatballs — it all depends on the sauce you use.

What you will need

- 1½ cup of water
- ¾ cup of millet
- 1 small yellow onion, finely diced
- 4 cloves garlic, ground
- 1 tablespoon dried basil
- 1 teaspoon ground fennel seeds
- 1 teaspoon red pepper crushed flakes (optional)
- ¼ cup dried tomatoes, finely chopped
- ¼ cup artichoke hearts, finely chopped
- ¼ cup roasted pine nuts or walnuts, chopped into large pieces
- 1 teaspoon sea salt (optional)
- 1 pound whole-grain cereal spaghetti
- 1 jar (28 ounces or 828 ml) hot spaghetti sauce
- Fresh chopped parsley, for decorat

Process

- Preheat the oven to 375 ° F (191 ° C).
- To make the meatballs, combine the water and millet in a small saucepan and bring the water to a boil at high temperature. Reduce it to medium-low and cook the millet until it is tender about 20 minutes. If it is not tender after all the water is absorbed, add two or three tablespoons of water and let it cook for another five minutes.
- While the millet is cooking, sauté the onion in a large skillet at medium-high temperature until it becomes translucent and begins to brown, approximately for five minutes. Add the garlic, basil, fennel, and red pepper flakes (if you use it) and cook for another minute. Add dried tomatoes, artichoke hearts, and nuts (if you use them) and remove the pan from the heat.
- When the millet is ready, add it to the pan with the onion mixture, add the sea salt (if you use it) and mix well. Shape the mixture into balls using an ice cream spoon or a 1/3 cup measure and place them on nonstick baking paper.
- Bake for like 15 minutes, turn them over and continue baking until the millet balls are lightly browned, about 15 minutes more.

- To make the spaghetti while the meatballs are baking, cook the spaghetti according to the package instructions and drain it.
- Transfer the cooked spaghetti to a larger tray. Top with meatballs and spaghetti sauce. Garnish with parsley and serve.

114.   Oatmeal Seasoned with Vegetables

This tasty twist of traditional oatmeal contains a variety of vegetables and turmeric to start the day with a healthy breakfast.

What you will need

- 4 cups of water
- 2 cups of "cut" oatmeal (quick-cooking steel-cut oats)
- 1 teaspoon Italian spices
- ½ teaspoon Herbamare or sea salt
- 1 teaspoon garlic powder
- 1 teaspoon onion powder
- ½ cup nutritional yeast
- ¼ teaspoon turmeric powder
- 1½ cup kale or tender spinach
- ½ cup sliced mushrooms
- ¼ cup grated carrots
- ½ cup small chopped peppers

Process

- Boil the water in a saucepan.
- Add the oatmeal and spices and lower the temperature.
- Cook over low heat without lid for 5 to 7 minutes.
- Add the vegetables.
- Cover and set aside for 2 minutes.
- Serve immediately.

115.   Pumpkin toast

What you will need

- 6 corn or whole-grain tortillas
- 4 cups diced pumpkin
- ¼ cup freshly squeezed orange juice
- ½ teaspoon garlic powder
- 1 cup onion, chopped into small pieces
- ½ cup pepper, chopped into small pieces
- 3 cloves garlic, crushed
- 2 cups cooked black beans
- ½ cup purple cabbage, cut into strips
- ¼ cup cilantro, chopped
- ¼ cup sauce
- ¼ cup mexicorema or guacamole dressing

- Salt and pepper to taste

Process

- Preheat the oven to 350-400 degrees F (204 degrees Celsius).
- Place the pumpkin in a bowl and add the orange juice, garlic powder, and salt and pepper to taste. Mix well.
- Place the seasoned pumpkin on a tray covered with baking paper and bake for 25 minutes or until the pumpkin is tender and lightly browned.
- While the pumpkin is in the oven, sauté the onions and peppers in a pan for 5 minutes.
- Add the garlic and beans to the sauteed onions and peppers, stir and cook for 2 minutes.
- Bake the corn tortillas in the oven for 10 minutes or until they are crispy but not burned.
- Organize the tortillas on a plate. Add the sauce, the mixture of sauteed vegetable beans and the roasted pumpkin. Top with the purple cabbage, cilantro, and Mexican sauce or guacamole.

116.   Broccoli Burritos

What you will need

- 1 bunch of broccoli (about 2 cups)
- 1 can of 15 ounces (425 g) of chickpeas
- ½ cup roasted red peppers
- 3 tablespoons lemon juice
- 6 tortillas (flour or gluten-free)
- 6 tablespoons of sauce (more or less to taste)

Process

- Cut or break broccoli into corsages. Peel the stems and cut them into slices 1/2 inch (1.2 cm) thick. Steam them over boiling water only until it softens, about 5 minutes.
- Drain the chickpeas and place them in a food processor with peppers and lemon juice. Process them until they run out of lumps.
- Spread about 1/4 cup of the chickpea mixture in an omelet and place it face up in a large, hot pan. Heat the tortilla until soft, about 2 minutes.
- Distribute a line of cooked broccoli through the center of the tortilla and pour a little sauce over it. Fold the bottom of the tortilla up, then, from one side, roll the tortilla around the broccoli. Repeat steps 3 and 4 with the remaining tortillas.

What you will need

- 1 large eggplant
- 1 small yellow onion
- 1 package of 12 ounces (340 g) of mushrooms (white, cremini or small Portobelo)
- ½ cup vegetable stock or water
- Sea salt to taste (optional)

FOR THE SAUCE

- ⅓ cup natural peanut butter
- ¼ cup water or low sodium vegetable stock
- 1 teaspoon agave syrup
- 1 tablespoon low-sodium soy sauce (use wheat-free soy sauce if you are gluten sensitive)
- 1 tablespoon balsamic vinegar

Process

- Cut the eggplant into pieces of about 1 inch (2.5 cm) and soak them in ample salt water to cover for 15 minutes. In the meantime, cut and chop the onion thinly, splitting the mushrooms into four. In the water, sauté the onions until they are tender. Rinse the eggplant and drain it. Return the eggplant and mushrooms to the pan with the soaking liquid from the eggplant. Cover them and let them cook until the eggplant is soft (5 to 10 minutes). 7

- Remove the agave syrup, soy sauce, and vinegar when the mixture is smooth and creamy and blend until the mixture is lump-free again.
- Verse the sauce in the pan over the sauteed vegetables. Cook over low heat and stir until the sauce has thickened, covering the vegetables full for a minute or two. Serve hot rice and steamed beans or other green vegetables with your pick.

118.   Fettuccine with broccoli and pine nuts

What you will need

- 1 pound broccoli
- 8 ounces fettuccine (use gluten-free pasta if you are gluten sensitive)
- 4 large tomatoes, diced (or a can of 28 ounces or 794 grams of chopped tomatoes)
- 2 tablespoons pine nuts
- 4 large garlic cloves, minced
- ¼ teaspoon salt (optional)

- ¼ spoon red pepper flakes (or a pinch of cayenne)

Process

- Broccoli split or cut into corsages; peel and slice the stems. Steam the broccoli for about 5 minutes until it's tender.
- Boil the pasta until tender. Rapidly drain and rinse.
- While cooking the pasta, sauté for 1 minute the garlic, red pepper flakes or cayenne, and pine nuts in water. Add the tomatoes and cook for 7 minutes over medium heat. Add the broccoli.
- Spread the paste and cover it with the sauce on a large plate. Serve right away.

119. Pizza dough with whole wheat and black beans

What you will need

- ¾ cup black beans (approximately ½ of a 15-ounce can or 425 g)
- ⅓ cup of water
- 1⅔ cup of warm water
- 1¼ spoon of sugar (or sweetener of your choice, is optional, but recommended to feed the yeast)
- 2¼ teaspoon yeast

- 1½ cup bread flour
- 1 cup wheat flour
- ½ teaspoon salt (optional)

Process

- Rinse and drain the beans, then puree them in a blender or food processor with 1/3 cup of water until they are lump-free. Add water as needed (increasing 1 tablespoon at a time).
- Beat the hot water, sugar, yeast, and bean puree together.
- Mix the flours and salt, slowly add them to the yeast mixture (if you do not use a bread machine, stir while adding the flour mixture).
- Knead until the dough is elastic, let it rise, and cover it, at least for an hour.
- Shape the pizza dough into a non-greased, lightly greased baking sheet.
- Place the ingredients and the sauce or sauces on the dough formed.
- Bake for 20 minutes (or until the ingredients are cooked).

120.   Crushed Olives Paste

What you will need

- 2 cups unprocessed whole grain pasta (I like Jovial [optional: quinoa])
- 20 or more crushed, chopped and chopped olives
- 4 cloves garlic, minced
- 1 bunch of parsley with stems, all chopped
- 1 tablespoon red chili flakes (less than that if you don't like spicy)
- Water to heat olives, garlic and parsley (optional: oil)
- Salt and pepper, if you wish
- Green leafy vegetable of your choice (I love arugula)

Process

- Boil the water in a large pot, add the pasta, stirring occasionally.
- Wash the parsley, arugula (or another green leafy vegetable of your choice)
- Crush the garlic and chop the parsley.
- Crush the olives, remove the seeds and chop them lightly.
- When the pasta is cooked, drain it and set it aside.
- Heat the pan, add a little water and add 1 tablespoon (or less) of red pepper flakes, chopped parsley, garlic, and olives. Fry them for about 2 to 3

minutes, making sure you keep stirring this mixture — don't let the garlic burn.

- Add the cooked pasta and mix.
- Turn off the heat.
- Add the arugula and mix (the arugula will wilt or cook slightly by the heat of the pasta).

121. Acorn squash stuffed with quinoa, hazelnuts, and apples

What you will need

- 2 acorn squash
- ½ cup quinoa
- 1 shallot
- 1 apple
- ½ cup hazelnuts
- 2 cups spinach
- ¼ cup fresh mint
- 2 tablespoons apple cider vinegar
- ¼ teaspoon salt

Process

- Preheat the oven to 425 ° F (218 ° C).
- To roast the pumpkin: cut the upper stem of the pumpkin and then cut it in half. Use a large spoon

to remove the seeds. Cut it in rooms. Place the squash with the cut side down in a saucepan or tray. Add approximately ½ inch (1 cm) of water to the bottom of the pan. Grill at 425 ° F (218 ° C) for 35 to 45 minutes until the pulp is tender enough to remove. When that happens, remove it from the oven and set it aside to cool. While the pumpkin is roasted, you can make quinoa filling.

- For quinoa filling: Peel and chop the shallot. Combine them with quinoa in medium sauce bread. Cover and toast for about 5 minutes until the quinoa begins to "explode." Add 1 cup of water, cover and simmer for 10-12 minutes until quinoa is soft. Next, remove the lid and fluff. Let quinoa cool in the pan for a few minutes. While the quinoa is being cooked, prepare the remaining stuffing.

- To toast the hazelnuts: Place the hazelnuts in the oven at 425 ° F (218 ° C) and place them for 10 to 12 minutes, until they darken slightly. Remove them from the oven and let them cool. When they are fresh enough to handle, roll them in a clean kitchen towel. This will help the peels to peel off. You will want to remove at least half of the shells, as these are bitter. Throw them away. Cut the hazelnuts into large pieces.

- Remove the center of the apple and cut it into cubes. Cut the spinach and mint into large pieces. In a large bowl, combine the apple with the cider vinegar. Stir well to cover the apple. This will help prevent the apple from browning. When the pumpkin is cold enough to handle it, carefully drain the pulp, keeping the skin intact.
- To assemble the filling: Combine quinoa, hazelnuts, apple, mint, spinach, pumpkin pulp, and salt. Stir well to combine. Serve the filling in your pumpkin shells. Place them back on the baking sheet. Cover and bake the pumpkin at 350 ° F (177 ° C) for 5 to 7 minutes, only until it is hot and then serve.

122.   Grilled Eggplant Sandwich

What you will need

- 1 medium eggplant (or 2 small zucchini)
- 1 to 2 tablespoons low-sodium soy sauce (use wheat-free soy sauce if you are gluten sensitive)
- 1 tablespoon balsamic vinegar
- 8 large, thick slices of whole-grain bread or gluten-free bread
- 1 roasted red pepper, sliced

- 1 large roasted garlic head
- 4 teaspoons of Dijon mustard (optional)
- 4 leaves of red lettuce

Process

- Cut the eggplant diagonally into slices 1/4 inch (6 mm).
- Brush the eggplant slices with soy sauce and roast them on a grill or iron skillet seasoned over medium-high heat for 2 to 4 minutes on each side until they are soft and lightly browned.
- Remove them from the pan and sprinkle with vinegar. Set them aside. Toast the bread, if desired and spread 2 to 4 cloves of garlic in the lower slice, add a layer of grilled eggplant, folding the soft pieces to fit in the slice of bread.
- Top with slices of roasted red pepper and lettuce. Spread mustard over the top slice of bread, if desired, then complete the sandwich and serve.

123.   Stewed red bean and chickpea stew

What you will need

- 2 tablespoons dried onion
- 1 teaspoon dried garlic

- ½ teaspoon of turmeric
- ½ teaspoon cumin seeds, crushed
- 1 teaspoon crushed mustard seeds
- 1 celery stalk, chopped
- 1 medium carrot, chopped
- 2 small potatoes, cut into smaller cubes
- 1 teaspoon vegetable powder broth or a pinch of sea salt

Half

- ½ can of 15 ounces (425 g) sweet corn, rinsed and drained
- 1 15-ounce can (425 g) chickpeas, rinsed and drained
- 1 can of 15 ounces (425 g) red beans, rinsed and drained

Final

- A handful of fresh flat-leaf parsley, chopped
- Black pepper or Cayenne pepper
- 2 tablespoons coconut milk
- Green Onion Leaves
- 1 tablespoon nutritional yeast per serving

Process

- Combine the ingredients listed in the first table in a small pot. Add enough water to cover the vegetables. Boil and simmer for 8 minutes.
- Crush about 1/3 of the chickpeas with a fork.
- Now, add the rinsed and drained corn, crushed chickpeas, and red beans. Mix well. Boil and simmer for another 5 minutes. Add a little more water if necessary.
- When the stew is ready, mix the coconut milk with the chopped parsley and season with the pepper of your choice.
- Garnish with the green leaves of the onions and nutritional yeast.

124.   Pomodoro sauce with summer vegetables

What you will need

- 2 tablespoons water or vegetable stock (more, if necessary)
- 1 medium onion, diced
- ½ teaspoon fresh garlic, minced
- ¼ teaspoon red pepper crushed flakes (reduce the amount if you want less spicy)

- 1 red pepper, diced
- 1 small zucchini, diced
- 1 small yellow summer squash, diced
- 2 pounds (907 g) of fresh tomato, mashed in the blender
- 1 small tomato paste (6 ounces or 170 g)
- 3 tablespoons red wine
- 2½ teaspoons kosher salt
- ¾ teaspoon black pepper
- Fresh basil, chopped into large pieces to garnish

Process

- Heat the broth in a large pot, add the onion with water or broth and steam it for about five minutes or until it is almost golden brown. Add a little more water if necessary to prevent sticking to the pan. Add fresh garlic and crushed red pepper. Skip for another minute.
- Add the pepper, zucchini, and summer squash. Continue cooking, stirring occasionally, for three or four minutes, or until all the vegetables are barely tender. Add the tomato puree, tomato paste, and red wine. Let the mixture boil and stir thoroughly. Reduce to a simmer immediately and let it continue like this, without covering the pot, until the sauce is slightly thick.

- Use an immersion blender to process the sauce to the desired texture (slightly soft, however, a bit thick). Season with salt and pepper to taste. Decorate it with fresh basil. Serve over hot pasta.

CHAPTER EIGHT
Plant-based diet Sauces recipes

125.   Red applesauce and beet

Ingredient

- 2 cups unpeeled apple, diced or grated
- 1 cup boneless cherries or mixed berries
- 1 cup unpeeled grated beets
- 1 tablespoon date paste
- ½ teaspoon cinnamon
- 2 tablespoons of water

Process

- Place all the ingredients in a saucepan.
- Take to a boil and cook until apples and beets have softened for 10-15 minutes.
- Crush with a potato masher or process in a food processor for a smoother consistency.
- Serve alone or use it to decorate Halloween treats.

126.   Chile with "cheese" and sauce

This rich and creamy non-dairy "cheese" spread is so spectacularly delicious that you will be doing it over and over again. The striking flavors combine beautifully with the sauce. Together they can be served as a side dish of raw vegetables or oil-free baked tortillas for a healthy snack, which will satisfy the public.

What you will need

"CHEESE" UNTABLE

- 1 cup raw cashews
- 2 red peppers, roasted, with the peel and seeds removed
- ¼ cup fresh lemon juice
- 3 tablespoons nutritional yeast
- 1 teaspoon salt
- ½ teaspoon red pepper in crushed flakes, or to taste

SAUCE

- 1 ½ cups diced tomato
- ½ cup diced bell pepper
- ¼ finely sliced red onion
- ½ teaspoon grated garlic
- 1 tablespoon fresh lemon juice
- 1 tablespoon chopped fresh cilantro
- 1 teaspoon jalapeño, seeded and chopped
- Salt and fresh ground pepper

Process

"CHEESE" UNTABLE

- In a high-power blender, combine all the ingredients with two tablespoons of water and process everything until smooth.

SAUCE

- In a medium bowl, combine all the ingredients on the list until jalapeño. Season everything with salt and pepper to taste.

127.   Tomatillo green sauce

What you will need

- 8 small tomatillos (approximately 1 pound or 453 grams)
- ½ white onion, cut in half
- 1½ teaspoon ground garlic (approximately 3 small teeth)
- 1 jalapeño, cut in half and seeded
- ⅓ cup full of chopped cilantro
- 1 can (4 ounces or 113 grams) of chopped soft green chiles

OPTIONAL ADDITIONS

- ½ tablespoon ground cumin
- Salt and pepper to taste
- Jalapeño Seeds (to add spicily)

Process

- Preheat the grill. Cover a large baking sheet with foil.
- Prepare the tomatillos: remove their lanterns, wash them, and cut them in half.
- Place the tomatillos and onion upside down on the prepared baking sheet. Add the garlic and jalapeño to the tray.
- Roast for five to seven minutes or until everything is uniformly charred.
- In a blender or food processor, mix the charred ingredients, cilantro, and chiles until the sauce is smooth.

128.   Tomatillo green sauce

What you will need

- 8 small tomatillos (approximately 1 pound or 453 grams)
- ½ white onion, cut in half

- 1½ teaspoon ground garlic (approximately 3 small teeth)
- 1 jalapeño, cut in half and seeded
- ⅓ cup full of chopped cilantro
- 1 can (4 ounces or 113 grams) of chopped soft green chiles

OPTIONAL ADDITIONS

- ½ tablespoon ground cumin
- Salt and pepper to taste
- Jalapeño Seeds (to add spicily)

Process

- Preheat the grill. Cover a large baking sheet with foil.
- Prepare the tomatillos: remove their lanterns, wash them, and cut them in half.
- Place the tomatillos and onion upside down on the prepared baking sheet. Add the garlic and jalapeño to the tray.
- Roast for five to seven minutes or until everything is uniformly charred.
- In a blender or food processor, mix the charred ingredients, cilantro, and chiles until the sauce is smooth.

What you will need

- Zest and juice of an orange
- ½ cup maple syrup
- 1 bag (12 oz - 340 g) of fresh red cranberries
- 1 teaspoon cinnamon

Process

- In a small saucepan, add all the ingredients and let them boil. Reduce the temperature and simmer for 15 minutes or until the blueberries burst and the sauce begins to thicken.
- Transfer it to a bowl and refrigerate until it cools down, at least for an hour.

130. Cranberry Sauce

What you will need

- 1 quarter (946 ml) apple juice
- ¼ cup brown rice syrup
- ¼ cup maple syrup

- 8 tablespoons flaked agar
- 3 cups raw red cranberries
- 1 teaspoon cinnamon
- 1 lemon, use lemon juice, and grated rind
- 1 pinch of sea salt (optional)

Process

- Blend apple juice with rice syrup, maple syrup, and agar flake in a 3-liter casserole. Boil and whisk to dilute the dust.
- Remove the cranberries and cinnamon as the temperature drops. Cover and cook until the cranberries are soft for about 10 minutes.
- Remove from heat, add lemon juice and rind.
- Pour everything into a glass container or mold and put it in the fridge; it should take nearly two hours for the cranberry sauce to thicken.

131.   Thick Mushroom Sauce

What you will need

- 1 12 oz (340 g) package of tender white or portobello mushrooms
- 1 to 2 tablespoons low sodium soy sauce (use one without wheat if you are gluten sensitive)

- 2 tablespoons whole-grain wheat flour (use gluten-free flour if you are gluten sensitive)
- 1 to 2 cups of vegetable stock
- Salt or black pepper, to taste (optional)

Process

- Clean and cut the mushrooms, then skip them in water until they are soft (about 5 minutes).
- Mix the flour with 1/4 cup of broth until it is lump-free (you can shake it in a small plastic container with a tight-fitting lid).
- Add the remaining broth to the mushrooms, soy sauce, and about half of the flour mixture.
- Let the thick sauce simmer for 3 to 5 minutes, stirring regularly.
- If the sauce is not thick enough for your taste, add the remaining flour mixture and continue heating and stirring until it thickens.
- Serve hot (and as soon as possible).

132.   Tasty Shiitake Sauce

What you will need

- 1 cup of water
- ¼ cup red wine

- ½ cup chopped onion
- 2 to 4 minced garlic cloves
- 1 tablespoon low-sodium soy sauce (use it without wheat if you are gluten sensitive)
- ¼ teaspoon cumin
- 1 pound (453 g) of fresh shiitake mushrooms
- ½ teaspoon dried coriander
- 1½ tablespoon cornstarch (cornstarch) mixed with 1/3 cup of water (or another thickener such as arrowroot)
- ½ teaspoon chili powder
- Salt or pepper to taste (optional)

Process

- Steam the onions and garlic in 3 to 4 tablespoons of water until tender.
- Add the rest of the glass of water to the pan. Add the other ingredients, except mushrooms and thickener.
- Cook briefly (1 to 2 minutes). Add the mushrooms and set the temperature to low.
- Cover and simmer for 30 minutes.
- Thicken the mixture with water and corn starch.
- Serve over brown rice or your favorite whole-grain cereal.

What you will need

- 1 cup oat flakes (not instant)
- 1 15 oz (425 g) can of cannellini beans (also known as white beans)
- 2 to 2½ tablespoons cornstarch (cornstarch)
- 1 to 2 tablespoons nutritional yeast (optional)
- 1 to 2 tablespoons garlic and chili sauce (optional)
- 1¼ to 1½ cups of water

Process

- Rinse and drain the beans (to remove salt).
- Using a blender or food processor, start with the beans first, press several times, and then add the rest of the ingredients, reserving the water to add it slowly while increasing the processing speed and calibrating the dough thickness until run out of lumps and thick, pancake type.
- Pour the sauce over the top of your pizza, sprinkle with ground black pepper or smoked paprika and bake your pizza from 425 ° F (218 ° C) to 450 ° F (232 ° C) for 15 to 20 minutes (or until that is golden). Enjoy!

134.   Cheese-flavored cauliflower, millet and carrot sauce

What you will need

- 1 cup cauliflower (chopped, in ½ "or 1 cm pieces)
- ½ cup raw millet
- ⅓ cup raw carrot (diced)
- 2 cups of water
- 1 teaspoon garlic powder
- 1 teaspoon salt (optional)
- 2 tablespoons cornstarch (cornstarch)
- 2 tablespoons wet mustard
- 1 teaspoon red tabasco sauce
- 1 cup of water

Process

- Boil the first 5 ingredients in a small pot, then simmer them on the lowest temperature setting for 25 to 30 minutes. Turn off the heat and let stand for 10 minutes. Remove them and let them cool to room temperature. If necessary, drain them.
- Put the vegetable mixture in a blender or in a food processor (mash them a little with the back of a wooden spoon).
- Add the remaining ingredients, reserving the water to add it in small increments, gradually increasing

the processing speed until the mixture is a lump-free and thick dough, similar to that of a pancake.

- recipe yields about 3½ cups of sauce.

135.   Spicy Tomato Jam

What you will need

- 4 cups of grape or cherry tomatoes, cut in half
- ¼ cup pure maple syrup
- 2 cloves garlic, minced
- 1½ teaspoon ground cumin or to taste
- 1 teaspoon chopped fresh red chili (optional)
- ½ teaspoon crushed red pepper or to taste

Process

- In a medium saucepan, combine the tomatoes cut in half and the maple syrup over medium-low heat. Cook them for five minutes, or until the tomatoes begin to release their juices, stirring occasionally.
- Add garlic, cumin, ginger, red chili (if you use it), crushed red pepper, and sea salt. Stir everything well in the pan and simmer. Reduce heat to low, cover and simmer for 30 to 35 minutes, stirring every 5 to 10 minutes.

- Remove the lid and continue to simmer for 5 to 10 minutes to remove the excess liquid a little. Remove the mixture from the heat and let it cool. Transfer it to an airtight jar and store it in the refrigerator for up to a week.

CONCLUSION

Those who follow a plant-based diet may need a little more carefully to prepare their meals. It can make all the difference to equip yourself with some dietary knowledge. Read our guides on vegetarian protein sources, where you can get vitamin B12 as well as the best plant sources of omega-3, may be useful.

When you change your diet drastically, starting gradually may be beneficial–maybe adding two or three meals based on plants, or days, a week. It helps the body to adapt to new foods and shifts in the percentage of certain nutrients, such as fiber. It also allows you to experiment with new foods over a period of time and create some storecupboard staples.

MEDITERRANEAN DIET COOKBOOK FOR BEGINNERS

The Ultimate Quick and Easy Guide on How to Effectively Lose Weight, Prevent Heart Disease with MOUTHWATERING RECIPES to INCREASE ENERGY AND HEAL THE BODY FOR LIFELONG HEALTH

G.S. Van Leeuwen

INTRODUCTION 234

INTRODUCTION

Healthy living is a treasured luxury that doesn't come by itself. You have to schedule it. Nutrition plays a crucial role in supplying the body with essential nutrients for growth and development. While some foods are considered healthy and in large quantities are required, others may be excluded from a daily diet. So works a Mediterranean diet plan.

The most common type of healthy diet is the Mediterranean diet. Studies have proved that people in the Mediterranean region can attribute the secret of healthy living to their balanced diet and active lifestyles. Researches have also shown that not only does this diet alleviate chronic heart disease, it also increases life expectancy.

Today's habits show that most people prefer to eat fried, frozen, or tinned foods that contain saturated fats and sugar. Lifestyles often suggest that most people don't take the time to exercise. As a result, with an increased chance of heart disease, diabetes and cancers, many people are obese and unhealthy.

The Mediterranean diet plan does not reduce the food types that one eats. The diet advises wise choices regarding food. For starters, instead of tinned and frozen food, one should eat fresh fruit and vegetables.

The food plan is based on the pyramid Mediterranean diet. According to him, cereals, grains, pasta, vegetables, legumes, beans, fruit, and nuts are food products to be included in a daily diet. These nutritious goods are a rich source of carbohydrates, fabrics, vitamins, minerals, and proteins. The recommended milk, yogurt and cheese consumption, low to moderate, reduce excessive intake of saturated fats. Animal meat such as chicken and eggs shall be consumed regularly and red meat, several times a month. Fish is considered a better choice, since it is high in nutritional value.

Olive oil provides good fat, which is responsible for reducing blood cholesterol levels and maintaining a healthy heart. All these recommendations are in line with a regular diet recommendation in the Mediterranean diet plan. A balanced dietary intake through an active physical life. This is not to say that people did not find time to rest in the Mediterranean area. They also used the time to relax and socialize after each meal, unwittingly giving time for proper digestion and good health.

CHAPTER ONE
Understanding the Mediterranean diet

The Mediterranean diet is one of the propagated diets, but that many people still don't know. It is usually a very simple diet and one of the most suitable, since it involves small risks to health.

Your idea is very simple and clear, and you always get interesting results done in a correct and specified way. It is from this transition that you will achieve your goal of a healthy weight loss, always with a consistent schedule.

Let's bring about what it treats for those who don't know about this diet, and also other factors that may enhance its action. From this, you can change your reality in favor of a type of diet that is very appropriate even for those who don't seek weight loss themselves.

The Mediterranean diet includes a large number of fruits, vegetables, beans, nuts, seeds, bread and other cereals. In the Mediterranean diet, fruits and vegetables are usually grown locally. Raw or minimally processed fruits and vegetables are often consumed. Fruit and vegetables contain many essential vitamins and minerals as well as antioxidants which are essential for good health.

The primary source of fat for the Mediterranean Diet is the use of monounsaturated fat. Olive oil is monounsaturated fat which is a rich antioxidant source like vitamin E. Olive oil is used as an alternative to butter, margarine and other fats. Butter and cream in fact are used only on special occasions. In the Mediterranean diet, olive oil is used for cooking tomato sauces, vegetable dishes, salads, and frying fish.

What is the Mediterranean diet

The Mediterranean diet is a set of human-related skills, knowledge, practices and traditions, ranging from land to table, covering crops, crops and fishing, as well as preserving, processing and preparing food and, in particular, its consumption.

This diet's nutritional model has remained constant over time and space, with the main ingredients being olive oil, cereals, fresh or dried fruits and vegetables, a moderate proportion of meat, fish and dairy products, abundant condiments and wine or infusions accompanying their consumption at the table, always respecting the beliefs of each community.

The Mediterranean diet-whose name derives from the Greek word regular, which means the way of life-comprises not only food, as it is a cultural element that promotes social interaction, verifying that traditional meals are a cornerstone of customs celebrations and festive events. Additionally, the Mediterranean diet gave rise to a large body of knowledge, poems, choruses, tales and legends.

One of the few diets that affect the health of those who adopt it is the Mediterranean diet. As you'll know a little later, this isn't even a diet, but rather a lifestyle that can be practiced for life.

When we think about diets, thoughts about poverty, hunger and the intake of tasteless foods always come to mind. That should not however be the case. Diet is a diet in which we choose to focus on eating other foods while limiting or reducing the consumption of others. Dieting is a diet that can aim for weight loss as well as weight gain. In addition to reducing weight, the diet may also aim to improve the symptoms of a variety of medical conditions that are closely related to food. These include, for example, type 2 diabetes, high cholesterol, high blood pressure, metabolic syndrome and even cancer.

When we want to follow a particular diet or diet to improve our health, the changes we make must be long-term. The Mediterranean Diet is one long-term diet. Not even a diet; it is a diet that we choose to follow for a long time or for life.

History of the Mediterranean diet

In recent years, there has been increasing concern for their health among men and women in different countries around the world. Many men and women often paid more attention to their meals, as many people were more concerned with their general health. Both men and women basically make dietary choices to boost their overall health and wellbeing.

A significant number of these men and women became interested in the Mediterranean diet as people became more aware of their health and nutrition. Yes, if you're a person who appreciates the food-health relationship, you may have a keen interest in the history of the Mediterranean diet.

Before you can fully understand what the Mediterranean diet is all about, you have to be mindful that it is more of a philosophy than a single eating regimen. There is in fact no Mediterranean diet popular to all Mediterranean countries around the world. Instead, the "Mediterranean

Diet" consists of the foods that people consume together in the different nations of the region.

The Origins of the Mediterranean Diet

The concept of a Mediterranean diet derives from the eating habits and patterns of the people who populate Italy, Greece, Spain, France, Tunisia, Lebanon and Morocco. As a result, the Mediterranean diet also includes a huge variety of delicious foods. In reality, if a person chooses to embrace the Mediterranean dining scheme definition, or if a person chooses to pursue a Mediterranean diet system, he or she will have the ability to enjoy a vast range of scrumptious food.

The diet of the peoples who populated the Mediterranean Sea regions has, in fact, remained almost unchanged for well over a thousand years. The region's history is full of examples of men and women living longer than similarly situated people consuming alternate diets. Through the centuries, people in the Mediterranean Sea region have enjoyed longer lives at the same historical epoch than people in other parts of the world.

Foods and beverages which are indigenous to the geographic landmass surrounding the Mediterranean Sea are at the heart of the Mediterranean diet. In short, the development of the Mediterranean diet and dining pattern developed initially by providential. The region's people ate those foods naturally and understandably, and drank those beverages that were readily available in and around their homes.

Historical elements of the Mediterranean diet scheme

As already mentioned, the diet of the Mediterranean Sea region's peoples has remained essentially unchanged over the centuries. The Mediterranean diet is made up of a plethora of healthy food items including:

- Fresh fruit
- Fresh vegetables
- Low-fat nuts
- Whole grains
- Monounsaturated fat

The Mediterranean diet used by people for generation after generation, in a similar vein, excludes or limits certain food items that have been deemed harmful in recent scientific studies. These food items are less than desirable and include:

- Saturated fats
- Red and fatty meat
- Rich dairy products
- Fatty fish

The so-called Mediterranean diet is the historical evolution of the Mediterranean Sea basin through generations of cultures and civilizations.

Man learns to grow certain plant species 10,000 years ago, and domesticates certain animals, ceases to be nomadic and creates stable population settlements, usually in areas with good climate and water.

Nutrition is already expressed in many texts in the ancient civilizations of Babylon and Egypt. We make observations about foods that should or should not be eaten and one of them is also forbidden.

The basin of the Mediterranean is a crossroads of nations, languages, cultures, and religions. With various eating practices, diets, fasts, ritual meals, etc. Driven by Christianity, Judaism, and Islam.

The Greeks, Punics, and Romans entered the Mediterranean with wheat, vineyards, and olive trees.

The Germans the rice, citrus, eggplant and dried pasta Muslims butter.

American basic foods were imported from America, such as tomatoes, peppers, and potatoes.

Based on a natural balance of fish and vegetable meats, with plenty of fiber, few saturated fats, this slow and continuous sum of products has given rise to the now commonly called Mediterranean diet. Carbohydrates of fast and slow absorption with ample vitamins and unsaturated fats and complemented with minerals and trace elements.

The Mediterranean was the melting pot of cultures and cuisines, where everything was added. Nothing has stood out and the sun and sea have provided the strong diversity and variety It is a healthy, balanced and highly valued cuisine or diet.

Hopkin (English) together with Fujian, the 1931 Nobel Prize, found out what the essential components of a complete diet should be, and that there are other components such as vitamins that are part of the diet.

In the early twentieth century, advances in nutrition went faster than other sciences, seeking the welfare of the population.

Scientifically today the so-called Mediterranean diet is considered to be an excellent model of the role.

The cardiac disease had become a serious health problem at the turn of the 20th century. At that time, researchers studying the disease and its causes discovered a startling pattern: the incidence of heart problems was much lower in some Mediterranean countries, particularly Italy and Greece compared to America.

The basis of the Mediterranean diet

The explanation they postulated might be in their diet: rich in plants, including fruits, vegetables, whole grains, legumes, potatoes, nuts and seeds. A strong quantity of extra virgin olive oil and a modest quantity of fish, poultry, dairy and eggs, as well as red meat, rarely completed this tradition's foundation.

The scientific and nutritional interest in it is relatively recent and, like so many other items on this subject, it's supposed advantages have become almost magical forces due to the inflated word of mouth and tricky publicity.

How does the Mediterranean diet work?

A fiber-rich mixed diet with healthy fats and numerous fresh ingredients such as vegetables, Mediterranean salads, fish and fresh fruit should make our body slim. The Mediterranean diet scores with many important ingredients controlling blood lipids and reducing the risk of heart disease. Quite healthy for digestion are vegetables, fruits and salads. The menu also includes pasta, pizza, rice, legumes, cold-pressed olive oil, fresh herbs, and garlic.

The Mediterranean diet program is important: take the time to eat. So it is very important to have a slow and comfortable meal. It takes a lot of time for the Southern Europeans to cook and eat with great pleasure. Smart tactic-now studies have shown this as well: slow eating helps you lose weight. Because if you don't take your time, you also skip the natural feeling of satiety on your body and thus eat more calories unnecessarily.

Mediterranean diet also maintains healthy fat metabolism and reduces the cholesterol levels according to studies. Additionally, scientific research shows a positive correlation between the Mediterranean diet and the prevention of Alzheimer's. A US study has shown that foods such as vegetables, fruit, olive oil and the like can lower the risk of Alzheimer's disease.

The Mediterranean diet does not provide for a supplementary sports program. Calorie counting is not the order of the day, either-you can get enough of the right food. It should always be prepared freshly in the best case.

CHAPTER TWO

Living longer with a Mediterranean diet

The Mediterranean diet, supplemented with virgin olive oil or nuts such as nuts, hazelnuts and almonds, is more effective in preventing cardiovascular diseases than low-fat diets of all kinds.

We live in a society that is obsessed with seeking the elixir of eternal youth, but there is an inexorable biological reality: we are oxidizing and that is why our bodies are aging. It is up to us to faster or slower than this oxidation. There are no miracles. It is possible to live longer and in better health conditions, as long as we are willing to change certain habits.

People who adhere to a healthy diet like the traditional Mediterranean would be more likely to prevent depression, so nutrition could help treat that mental disorder, suggests an international team of researchers.

Public health, psychiatry, and nutrition specialists evaluated the role of dietary interventions in depression with the intention of developing recommendations for future psychiatric health care, as the disorder carries high social costs.

The researchers conducted a systematic review of indices and results from 41 longitudinal and cross-sectional studies on healthy diet compliance with depressive symptoms or clinical depression, which attempted to synthesize the link between food quality and disorder.

The researchers from the United Kingdom, France, Australia and Spain conclude that a diet based on fruits, vegetables, grains, fish, nuts and olive oil, but without too much meat or dairy, seems to have advantages in terms of mood.

Dr. Camille Lasalle of University College London points out the evidence that the food we eat can make a difference in reducing our risk of depression.

Experts in metabolic medicine say more rigorous and specific trials are needed to confirm evidence of the possible connection and determine whether depression can be treated with diet.

In fact it is complicated to explain the link between mood and food, as there are many factors that may be involved.

Depression can cause loss of appetite and someone who feels bad cannot take care of it as well, while happy people can be more likely to lead healthier lifestyles, including not drinking alcohol is a depressing mood known to them.

Eating bad foods, lots of sugar and highly processed foods may increase the risk of depression, which means eliminating them from the diet is important.

Research on the traditional Mediterranean diet has shown that it can reduce our risk of developing diseases like type 2 diabetes, hypertension and high cholesterol, all of which are risk factors for cardiac diseases.

The researchers have discovered that people closely following a Mediterranean diet would live longer and have less chance of gaining weight.

Health Benefits of the Mediterranean Diet

1. Lower risk of heart disease

Olive oil is the main ingredient in cooking and Mediterranean flavor. Olive oil contains monounsaturated fats, which for a healthy heart are a good component. In comparison, eating foods high in saturated fat leads to heart disease growth. Instead of butter, many Mediterranean dishes are cooked with oil and sauces and dressings include olive oil as one of the principal ingredients.

Mix various types of balsamic spoonfuls of vinegar with oil- of whatever flavor you like and you'll get a healthy salad dressing. There's no need to buy premixed dressings filled with unnecessary fats when you can create a healthy one with just a few ingredients, simply and easily. Therefore, the fresher it is, the better and a delicious salad dressing is produced if you use a little olive oil and balsamic vinegar.

2. Lower risk of having diabetes

Olive oil has many benefits for the skin. Since Mediterranean diets use it in different ways, if you follow the diet to the letter, you'll surely benefit from it. Some research studies have shown that olive oil and the Mediterranean diet, in particular, could help reduce the risk of developing type 2 diabetes.

Researchers believe a large number of rich minerals and phytochemicals in the Mediterranean diet can decrease insulin resistance and inflammation. Your body needs to successfully break down the sugars. If the body can't do this properly, the risk of suffering from type 2 diabetes could be greater.

3. Prevents hypertension

All you consume directly affects your blood pressure and there are foods in the Mediterranean diet that can help lower the pressure. Additionally, this diet consists of healthy foods that don't increase blood pressure. Genetics can play an important role in whether or not you have hypertension although it is not very good to have an unhealthy diet that contains a lot of fat and salt.

Unnecessary sodium will not be consumed in the Mediterranean diet by not eating processed foods which will increase blood pressure and hold it at very high levels. Hypertension can cause hypertension and other cardiovascular diseases so this diet can help you to reduce the serious health risks involved.

4. Prevents fatty liver disease

A diet rich in processed foods that contain salt, sugar, calories and unhealthy fats is practiced by many people. Adopting such an unhealthy diet increases the risk of developing obesity, which is the main cause of fatty liver disease. The amount of olive oil in the Mediterranean diet helps to remove many saturated fats from the diet and, at the same time, prevents fatty liver diseases.

Interestingly, the diet does not include red meat, as it contains a lot of saturated fat. Alternatively, mineral-rich chicken and fish are the meats preferred by this diet. Everything you eat and how much you eat of something the liver has difficulty processing (such as red meat) can lead to other liver diseases.

5. A potentially longer lifespan

Some studies link longevity with the Mediterranean diet. Diet can also reduce the risk of cardiovascular disease, which ultimately helps people live longer lives. Then start eating more fresh produce, nuts, seeds and olive oil to reap health benefits, including the possibility of living longer and reducing the chances of heart problems. While it is obviously desirable to start and maintain this diet in youth throughout life, research has shown that it can also have a positive effect on those who start eating it in later life.

6. Improvement of cognitive function

The research suggests a correlation between the foods present in the Mediterranean-style diet and the improvement of brain functions, as well as a lower rate of decline in mental health. As we age, cognitive functions decrease and this sometimes leads to extremely serious conditions such as Alzheimer's disease or the appearance of dementia.

It's also common to experience a mild memory loss and misunderstanding spells when you're older and this isn't considered a sign of a neurological disorder. The Mediterranean diet can help you to stay mentally active given your age, to fully enjoy life and potentially reduce the normal effects of aging.

7. Lower risk of cancer

It has also been linked to reducing the risk of developing and dying from certain types of cancer, in addition to all other serious diseases that the Mediterranean diet may help to reduce. Eating lots of fruits and vegetables is an important component of the diet, which is one of the reasons you can reduce your cancer risk-most fruits and vegetables are rich in antioxidants.

It is understood that antioxidants are anti-carcinogenic. Nuts and oils in the Mediterranean diet also play an important role in reducing inflammation and insulin differentiation, which may inhibit the growth of certain types of cancer.

8. Reduction of preservatives and chemicals

The Mediterranean diet is filled with fresh produce, vegetables and fruits, meats delivered straight from the butcher shop, and ocean-fresh fish. It means we do not consume precooked and processed foods that typically contain a lot of additives and preservatives that are not safe for anyone.

If you want to see something as simple as a frozen chicken package, there are usually multiple lines in the ingredient list you don't eat only chicken. In addition to salt, fat, sugar and calories, precooked foods bring other potentially harmful ingredients into your body. Any foods that can be harmful to your health will be eliminated following a Mediterranean-style diet.

9. Increased consumption of antioxidants

Antioxidants, nowadays, are a phenomenon. List after list of super-foods includes antioxidant-rich components. These have been linked to lowering the risk of certain types of cancer and the benefits don't stop there-they have natural anti-inflammatory properties and can help prevent heart disease, decrease the risk of developing diabetes and boost the immune system. They also possess anti-aging properties.

That's a fantastic list of potential benefits and eating more fresh fruits and vegetables is all you need to do. Explore the various types and stuff you've never eaten before. There's no reason I couldn't explore new food!

10. Less likely to suffer from Parkinson's disease

There is some debate as to whether or not the diet in the Mediterranean style may minimize the risk of Parkinson's disease developing, but there are enough scientists who believe that there is a link worth considering.

A study published in the American Journal of Clinical Nutrition found that the development of diseases such as

Parkinson's and Alzheimer's had decreased by 13 percent when participants followed a Mediterranean diet, which is a fairly large number in general terms. The exact diet portion that reduces this risk has not been established but the facts are insight.

Losing Weight with the Mediterranean Diet

There are many different types of diets, perhaps even too many. However, experts say you should pay attention to the healthiest ones, which also provide nutrients to your body in addition to helping you lose weight. Mediterranean diet-making friends with it are worthwhile, because it is a great example of this. Don't forget this approach!

The Mediterranean diet is rich in protein, fiber, omega-3 fatty acids, whole grains, minerals, vitamins, and most importantly, it contains almost no fat, carbohydrate, and industrial flour. Let's look at it deeper.

How can a Mediterranean diet help me lose weight?

- First of all, the strict Mediterranean diet is not the same as weight loss. This diet is synonymous with the development of very healthy eating habits and thanks to the ingredients found therein, we learn to control body weight and exclude everything else that can lead to weight gain and even diseases from the diet. Nutritionists suggest you can lose weight just one kilogram a week by using this type of diet.

- In other words, the Mediterranean diet is not only helpful to us but also to our entire family. The World Health Organization (WHO) proposed the basic principles of the so-called healthy eating pyramids.
- The advantages of a Mediterranean diet are the product of the excellent quantity of healthy fats. These are just monounsaturated fats that are present in olive oil and fatty acids like Omega 3 and 6.
- That diet excludes both animal protein and red meat.
- The richest in antioxidants is the Mediterranean diet: fruits, dried fruits, vegetables and legumes.
- This contains a good amount of fiber.
- The Mediterranean diet helps to reduce cholesterol in the body, protects against cardiovascular disease and takes care of your weight due to a healthy amount of nutrients that removes unhealthy fat.

CHAPTER THREE
Starting the Mediterranean Diet

The first step in getting the Mediterranean diet started is to learn its foundations, that is, the ingredients that make it up and make it one of the world's healthiest choices.

1. Olive oil as a fat preference

Rich in vitamin E, monounsaturated fatty acids and antioxidants, the Mediterranean diet's essential oil is this. For example, it is used to season salads, fry, toast and all that needs some form of fat for seasoning or cooking!

So if you're thinking about starting the Mediterranean diet, leave the butter and heat the olive oil.

2. Daily consumption of plant foods

For their significant contribution of minerals, vitamins, fibers and antioxidants, grains, fruits, vegetables and nuts are eaten every day and regularly. However, according to the Mediterranean diet food pyramid, each main meal should include: 1-2 fruits More than 2 vegetable servings, natural or cooked. Preferably, at least one raw daily portion.

3. Daily cereal consumption

One or two portions of cereal are recommended per meal, preferably whole grain in the form of rice, pasta, bread, couscous or other types, for example. The carbohydrates derived from these foods will, of course, provide the necessary energy to face the day.

4. Choose fresh, seasonal foods

The purchasing and use of fresh and seasonal foods allow us to enjoy their nutrients, taste and fragrance. Use foods that are unprocessed and seasonal. It is a safe step and is environmentally friendly.

5. Moderate consumption of red meat

Because of the health problems that animal fat intake can create, moderate consumption of red and processed meat is recommended. Therefore, according to the Mediterranean diet, the saturated fats of these meats must be reduced.

6. Daily consumption of dairy products

Yogurt and cheese are a daily part of the Mediterranean diet and contain important minerals such as calcium and phosphorus, vitamins and proteins with a high biological value.

7. Fish two times a week and eggs, three or four

Starting with the Mediterranean diet, it's important to reduce your consumption of red meat and instead eat fish, for example, for its content of Omega-3 fatty acids and eggs, sources of quality protein.

8. Bakery and sweets products, very low consumption

It's not a matter of removing these ingredients from your diet entirely, but note that your consumption should be extremely moderate. In fact, it recommends fewer than two servings a week.

9. Water as a preferred drink

Water is a key Mediterranean diet pillar and should be your favorite drink. Furthermore, wine is also part of this diet, consumed in moderation and usual fashion.

10. Physical exercise

A good diet is not the only thing that you need to look for to enjoy good health. Therefore, n will make sure to exercise daily and regularly to enjoy the benefits of a healthy diet.

CHAPTER FOUR

Eat Well and Stay Healthy the Mediterranean Way

The Mediterranean diet is an eating style that can help you lose weight and improve your health. Typically eaten in countries and regions bordering the Mediterranean sea, it is based on diet. This emphasizes fruits, vegetables, whole grains, and legumes while including smaller amounts of meat, poultry, dairy and sweets. Several studies have shown that the Mediterranean diet will help you lose weight and reduce the risk of heart disease, cancer, Parkinson's disease, and Alzheimer's. Adopting a lifestyle and diet in a Mediterranean style will help you eat better and stay healthy.

Adopting a Mediterranean Style Diet

Use the foods more focused on plants. Eating more plant-based foods is one of the main components of the Mediterranean diet. These types of foods will make up the majority of your diet.

Foods based on plants include a wide variety of foods—some high in protein, fiber, and many vitamins and minerals.

Most of all eat: fruits, vegetables, whole grains, nuts, peas, beans, lentils... At each meal and snack you should include one or more of those food groups.

In the Mediterranean diet nuts and seeds are especially common. These contain a large amount of protein, minerals, and heart-healthy fats. Include 1–2 table cubits per serving (14.8–29.6 ml).

Citrus fruits are another prevalent plant-based food in the Mediterranean diet. Lemons, limes, oranges, and grapefruits have large amounts of vitamin C, a potent antioxidant that has been shown.

Replace butter with heart-sanctioning oils. Another trademark of the Mediterranean diet is the use of a great deal of olive oil. It is used for cooking as well as dressing up various foods.

Butter is a less nutritious choice than olive oil, since it is very high in saturated fat. Some studies have linked higher saturated fat levels to heart disease.

On the other side, olive oil is thought to be a superior and more nutritious type of fat. It is very rich in monounsaturated fats that have been linked with reduced heart disease risk.

While olive oil is a healthier fat option, it is still fat, and should be weighed when you use it. One serving is one tablespoon and the portions should be limited to two or three per day.

Red meat limit. Red meat consumption in the US is higher than in a lot of other countries. The Mediterranean diet generally only occasionally includes red meat — perhaps once or twice a month.

Red meat was associated with a range of adverse health effects when eaten in large quantities (such as heart disease and diabetes). A study recently found that high amounts of red meat are associated with a shortened life span.

Substituting other sources of protein (such as tofu, rice, nuts, or eggs) was associated with a reduced risk of heart disease and diabetes.

Include products made with low-fat dairy. The dairy products are another great source of protein found in the Mediterranean diet. During the day throw in a serving or two of them.

Low-fat dairy contains a lot of protein but there are also high amounts of calcium, vitamin D and potassium in these foods.

Yogurt, cheeses, milk or cottage cheese may be included in dairy products.

Measure the proper serving of dairy foods. Attach 1/2 cup yogurt, 1 oz cheese, or 6 oz low-fat milk to taste.

At least eat fish twice a week. The Mediterranean diet also stresses the consumption of fish and shellfish, in addition to eating several different sources of plant-based proteins.

Most diets in the Mediterranean style recommend eating at least twice a week fish or shellfish. Include dinner with a 3-4 oz serving of fish or shellfish.

Many shellfish and fish are larger in omega-3 fats. A particular type of fat was associated with a reduced risk of heart disease, a reduction in blood pressure, cholesterol and triglyceride.

All seafood is a great choice and particularly high in heart-healthy fats are fish such as salmon, tuna, mackerel, and sardines.

Cook instead of salt, with herbs and spices. Salt improves your food's taste, but using more herbs and spices like the Mediterranean diet also adds a lot of flavor to your food without the salt added. Salt increases the risk of hypertension which can lead to heart disease or stroke. Herbs have no adverse effects, and are useful in the diet.

Basil: This herb is very rich in essential oils and phenolic compounds that have anti-inflammatory properties and can relieve chronic inflammation such as arthritis. It is also rich in beta-carotene, lutein and vitamin A, which protect the body in an exceptional way against free radicals.

Marjoram: This plant was used for a wide range of ailments including colds, symptoms of menopause relief, cramps of the stomach and gas.

Oregano: This herb was associated with reducing disorders of the respiratory tract, GI disorders, PMS symptoms, and urinary tract infections. It is also high in fatty acids such as magnesium, dietary fiber, calcium, manganese, vitamin c, A and omega-3.

Peregrine: This common herb was thought to help prevent cancer, diabetes and improve the health of bones. It also contains high quantities of vitamins A, K, and C.

Sage: In addition to potentially lowering blood glucose and cholesterol levels, this herb may reduce cognitive ailments like Alzheimer's and dementia.

Thyme: This herb may be effective against infection by fungi, especially those around your toenails. It may also help to reduce acne, high blood pressure and certain cancers.

Mint: This plant can help with digestion, alleviate seasonal allergies and prevent

Rosemary: The herb will improve the immune system and aid with digestion. It has anti-inflammatory properties that can decrease the severity of asthma attacks and increase blood flow to your brain, which can enhance cognitive problems.

Garlic: This spice has been involved in numerous health benefits such as the lower risk of heart disease and artery hardening, reducing high cholesterol, lowering the risk of heart attack and lowering the risk of high blood pressure.

Indulge in a glass of wine. In addition to raising your HDL (the "healthy" cholesterol), and preserving your coronary arteries, drinking wine in moderation will reduce your chances of developing cardiovascular diseases.

Several research studies have shown that the right amounts of wine consumption— one glass (5 oz) or less per day— have its benefits.

Wine helps dilate the arteries and increase blood flow within your body. Wine phenols also aid in reducing bad cholesterol. When you drink alcohol, try drinking one 5-ounce glass of wine per day.

Eat smaller portions. The portions that are usually served in the US are much greater than required. Large large portions, when consumed, can lead to excess calorie intake, weight gain and obesity.

Smaller portions of the Mediterranean diet include. Such smaller portions can help keep calories low and reduce weight or maintain weight.

Measure portions of all groceries. To stay on track, you can use a food scale, or weigh cups. Guessing or "eye-balling" portions usually results in larger portions than is required.

Protein foods should be 3-4 oz per serving, vegetables 1 cup or 2 cups of leafy greens, fruit 1/2 cup and grains 1/2 cup per serving as well.

Exercise regularly. People are far more involved in the countries bordering the Mediterranean than in the US. Their increased level of activity is partly the reason why they consider their lifestyle very healthy.

Physical activity has been associated with many health benefits, including increased levels of high-density lipoprotein (HDL or "healthy" cholesterol), decreased levels of triglycerides, decreased risk of diabetes and high blood pressure, enhanced arthritis-related pain, and decreased cancer rates.

Seek to do aerobic exercise of moderate intensity at least for 30 minutes during each session five days a week. This will help you meet the US minimum physical activity requirement of 150 minutes per week.

Take up walking, running, cycling, swimming, and hiking to get aerobic exercise. Include two to three days of 20-minute strength training every week.

You should also try pilates or yoga that will help build your strength and flexibility.

Walk and move more throughout the day. People living in the Mediterranean are taking part in more leisure practices compared to people living in the US. It has been shown that being more active over the day has similar benefits to aerobic activity.

Lifestyle practice is the activity that you embed in your daily routine. Taking the stairs, for example, or mopping down the concrete, are called lifestyle behaviors.

Throughout their days' Mediterranean people tend to have more activity in the lifestyle. For instance, we're cycling to and from destinations, or riding a bike instead. Involvement is an essential part of your daily routine.

Think of your day, the schedule for your work and the whole week. Where can you put in more movement or more steps? Can you ride a motorcycle to work? Can you go to the drugstore or grocery store? You should take the stairs instead of the lift? Try to incorporate more moves into your day.

Eat mindfully. Another feature of a Mediterranean diet and lifestyle is that they usually eat more carefully compared to the American hustle and bustle. Conscious eating can help eat less, enjoy eating more and even help you lose weight.

It's a way to eat carefully. It's a way to eat that makes you more aware of what kind of food you consume, how much you eat and how easily you eat.

Take 20 minutes to eat your meal, remove distractions from your dining area (e.g., TVs or cell phones), take small bites, chew more thoroughly, and adjust your body's sense of satiety.

Manage stress. Chronic lifestyle stress can be tough to deal with. Studies have shown, however, that people living in Mediterranean countries can deal with stress better and suffer less from heart disease.

Try to tackle as much tension as possible. Try to listen to music, exercise, meditate, do yoga, or converse with a friend or family member.

When stress management is too complicated, or if you are unsure how to deal with stress, see a life coach or therapist for additional assistance.

When talking about the Mediterranean diet, the evolution of the human species over the centuries must be taken into account, which has brought about many changes both in their way of life and in their relationship with the rest of the species, as well as in the transformation of their diet reflected in changes in food depending on geographical areas.

In human history there has been a long transition from prehistoric hunters and gatherers to the present day. Throughout post-industrialized societies, major changes have occurred which are also reflected in the diet and nature of human nutrition.

In different cultures it is possible to recognize certain features that make their diet a lifestyle. This is done with the popular Mediterranean diet, a diet that combines various ingredients from local agriculture through recipes and special methods of healthy cooking.

Instead of a food program, the popular and world-famous Mediterranean diet is a cultural heritage that encourages you to lead a healthy lifestyle consisting of a variety of ingredients used to prepare recipes focused on exercise in seasonal, natural, and local items with moderate physical activity.

As its name suggests, this diet is born in the villages of the Mediterranean basin, transmitted from generation to generation for centuries and changing and incorporating new techniques of food and cultivation according to the geographical location of these populations.

The Mediterranean Diet's basic ingredients make up a perfect "wheat-vine-olive" triangle to which vegetables, legumes, fruits, fish, cheeses, and nuts are added and olive oil is the main source of fats. The Mediterranean Diet offers enough macronutrients to the body through a healthy and varied diet plan.

CHAPTER FIVE

Mediterranean Diet Food Pyramid Vs Traditional Food Pyramid

For most of us, the food pyramid contains the most recognized symbol of healthy food. This demonstrates which foods we can consume in which portion size so our body gets the nutrients these needs. If you are designing a healthy diet plan you will do well to look at the pyramid of Mediterranean diet foods.

What is the Mediterranean Diet Food Pyramid?

The Mediterranean diet food pyramid is an alternative to the conventional one that is becoming increasingly popular because it is not based on popular trends in the food industry. The diet itself is centered within the Mediterranean region, on thousands of years of tradition. Mediterranean countries ' dietary traditions have long been recognized as being very healthy, and the food they eat is one of the main factors in that healthiness. Being aware of the difference between the traditional food pyramid and the Mediterranean one will help you improve your health.

The Mediterranean diet pyramid is substantially different from the traditional one we are familiar with. Several glaring discrepancies, namely;

- The Mediterranean one has no fats category Red meat is at the top of the Mediterranean pyramid as a food to eat with sweets / desserts at least.
- Olive oil is grouped with fruit and vegetables as something to be frequently consumed

The top portion of the Mediterranean diet food pyramid starts with red meat as an animal protein source. Red meat and candy are the Mediterranean's least-eaten foods, around 2-3 times a month. The next group, eaten a few days a week, includes meat, eggs and dairy products such as cheese and yogurt. Next come fish and seafood eaten almost daily. The Mediterranean diet is basically low in saturated fats and high in monounsaturated fats, and high in omega 3.

The lower pyramid level consists of fruits, vegetables, legumes (beans), nuts, seeds, herbs, spices, whole-grain bread, whole-grain pasta, couscous, brown rice, polenta, and other whole grains. The Mediterranean people rarely eat processed grains (i.e., white flour). A wide number of these fresh foods are consumed every day, and are usually either raw or cooked slightly. Which ensures nutrients remain intact. Cooking foods actually kills or makes most nutrients indigestible. Hence eating raw or partially cooked food is always safer.

The main aspect of the Mediterranean pyramid is to prescribe six glasses of water per day and a moderate amount of wine (i.e. one glass of red wine with dinner).

It is interesting to note that in the Mediterranean pyramid, olive oil is grouped with fruits and vegetables. As you can imagine, olive oil is an essential part of the Mediterranean diet and includes many dishes. While it is true that oil is high in calories, olive oil is a good, monounsaturated fat that is high in antioxidants and contains omega-3 fatty acids, so we can consume a little more as long as we don't go crazy. Monounsaturated oils like olive oil are anti-inflammatory and help with diseases like asthma and arthritis. These are also safer in the heart because Omega 3 lowers LDL ("bad") cholesterol and increases HDL ("good") cholesterol. Less natural olive oil.

You may wonder how Mediterranean people receive their iron, as they don't eat a lot of red meat. The response to this is the same as a vegetarian is. Also good sources of iron are legumes (beans) and green leafy vegetables, and the Mediterranean diet is full of these healthy foods. Nevertheless, the whole Mediterranean diet food pyramid is made up of healthy foods that ensure that those who adopt the Mediterranean diet enjoy optimal health.

We are all involved in being lean, losing weight, getting a good diet plan, getting rid of cardiovascular and health-related illnesses. Typically, once you have a good diet plan such as the Mediterranean diet pan, the chances are that you will eventually reduce the number of calories in your body resulting in decreased heart-related issues.

The other benefits include weight shedding, fat burning and gradually slimming down. It is truly easy to implement diet plans like the Mediterranean diet plan. That's because you can't eat the gunk and bland vegetables that many people have to submit to just because they want to live longer and healthier.

You will enjoy delicious meals with the Mediterranean diet plan while still rising the chances of getting heart-related problems. Here are a few tips to help adopt the Mediterranean diet.

1. Decide on What Diet Type

Most of the people tend to worry about their diet plans consistently. They worry if it will work if they lose weight if they can reduce their chances of dying younger as a result of heart disease and cancer and, most importantly, worry if they can keep up with their diets. Okay, the thing is, if you really want to do this, you have to choose which choice you think works best for you.

There are two main dietary forms or regimens. You can do the form planned or the style Do-It-Yourself. It all depends on the makeup you have. For instance, some people don't like strict time tables and are more likely to fail to use them because they are instinctively opposed to things that make them feel like they're boxed in.

Though, other people find it exciting to chart a strategy and are more likely to stick to it. It all depends on the person that you are. So, whatever happens, just pick one out. If you don't know which group you're moving for, just go for one. You can always turn to the other, if you don't like it.

2. Find Recipes that Will Work for You

The taste of the people in the food is different. You need to find and stick to that which works for you. The basic components of the Mediterranean diet plan include, among others, olive oil, legumes, vegetables, nuts, grains, unprocessed carbohydrates, fish, reduced red meat consumption and saturated fat.

Now, if you just like eating them like that, then it's all right. But if you want to make it much more fun, you'd have to find recipes that work. The South Beach Diet recipes, for example, are great and fun to cook. So, find recipes that inculcate these and which are based on the Mediterranean diet.

3. Get Creative With the Diet

Since following a few diet plans, the reason many people return to eating junk is that the diets are either dull, repetitive or lacking in flavor. So, what you should do is just go for those delicious meals. Get yourself creative with the recipes. Try something new, and something different. Chances are if you're looking well enough, you'll find lots of Mediterranean diet recipes that will last you for a whole year and more.

4. Be Disciplined

Because the Mediterranean diet is really simple to use and apply, it is hardly called a diet by some. I just see it as an alternative lifestyle and food choices that help you stay healthy and live longer. The secret, then, is discipline. Stay focused and who knows, you could just give yourself an extra 15 years of health and life.

CHAPTER SIX

Reasons Why a Mediterranean Diet in the 21st Century Is A Healthy Choice

If you're a person on a quest for a solid diet plan, you may feel exhausted a lot of the time. It is almost impossible for a person to turn on a TV set or open a newspaper in the 21st century, without being bombarded with ads for a variety of different diet plans and items.

With the vast number of diet plans, services, supplements and aids on the market, a diet plan that can and will better meet your needs now and into the future may seem almost impossible to choose. Most significantly, it can be difficult to discern whether one or the other of these different diet plans are actually a healthy path to follow. In many cases, fad diets are not really focused on the foundations of a healthy life.

When you decide what sort of diet plan or a diet plan or diet will best serve your needs and enhance your health in the future, you will want to look at the benefits that the Mediterranean diet can offer.

While there are multiple reasons why a balanced alternative is a Mediterranean diet, there are five main reasons why a good choice is a Mediterranean diet.

1. The benefits of fruits, vegetables, fiber and whole grains

Regular consumption of fresh fruit and vegetables is an important component of the Mediterranean diet. Medical experts and nutritionists generally agree that a person should eat around 5-6 servings of fresh fruit and vegetables (or steamed items) daily.

People who generally adhere to the Mediterranean diet eventually eat more than the minimum recommended amount of fruit and vegetables. As a result, nutritionists in different parts of the world have prescribed a Mediterranean-based program for its customers. Today doctors who recommend healthy eating habits to their patients often stick to the Mediterranean diet.

The Mediterranean diet contains healthy amounts of dietary fiber and whole grains, in addition to fruit and vegetables. Fiber and whole grains have proven effective in reducing heart disease incidence and certain types of cancer.

2. The benefits of olive oil - avoiding saturated fat

Many people have a simple misperception of the Mediterranean diet. The Mediterranean diet is high in fat, many people have heard. There is some reality in the definition, on some point, that the Mediterranean diet is higher in fat than some other diet programs. A person who follows the Mediterranean diet takes from fat about thirty percent of their daily calories. (Most diets advised the consumption of fat calories at a rate of approximately thirteen to fifteen percent per day. Moreover, some diets envisage the intake of animal fat.)

The vast majority of the fat a person consumes on the Mediterranean diet comes from olive oil. The fat present in the Mediterranean diet is not, in other words, the unhealthy saturated fat that can cause disease, obesity and other health concerns. Nonetheless, research has shown that there are a variety of solid benefits of olive oil consumption, including a decrease in the risk of breast cancer incidence in women.

3. Dairy in moderation

While in some cases it can be helpful to eat low-fat or non-fat dairy products, many people worldwide rely on heavy creams, eggs, and other fatty dairy products for their daily diets. The Mediterranean diet has low milk content. All dairy products which are currently on the menu are actually low in fat. A person who consumes four eggs a week is considered an extremely heavy eater of the eggs.

4. Red Meat in Moderation

Very little red meat is included in the Mediterranean diet. This diet depends on moderate amounts of lean poultry and fresh fish when it comes to meat products. As a result, people on the Mediterranean diet have lower levels of "bad" cholesterol and higher levels of "good: cholesterol". Furthermore, thanks to the inclusion of lean and fresh fish in the diet, the members of the Mediterranean diet enjoy the antioxidant benefits present in some oils and fish products.

5. A Well Balanced Dieting Scheme

Ultimately, the Mediterranean diet is gaining worldwide acclaim from experts and adherents as it is a balanced diet program. Study after study shows that a balanced diet low in fat which includes fruit, vegetables, whole grains and lean meatworks to ensure complete health and well-being.

A weekly menu based on the Mediterranean diet

Monday

- Breakfast: Coffee with milk. Toast with goat cheese spread. Apple.
- Mid-morning: cereal bar. Natural Orange Juice
- Food: Chickpea soup. Hake meatballs stewed with potatoes. Grapes.
- Snack: Cottage cheese with sugar.
- Dinner: Swiss chard with garlic. Grilled turkey and tomato cherry skewers with couscous. Custard apple.

Tuesday

- Breakfast: Milk with cocoa powder. Whole grains
- Mid-morning: Natural pear smoothie.
- Food: Stewed green beans. Grilled chicken fillet with steamed broccoli. Pineapple Carpaccio.
- Snack: Toast with quince jam.
- Dinner: Salad with cucumber, black olives, onion, and Feta cheese. Salmon with papillote vegetables. Peach.

Wednesday

- Breakfast: Milk Crispbread with strawberry jam.
- Mid-morning: Sandwich with lettuce, tomato, and cheese. Natural grape juice.
- Food: Tomato soup. Broth rice with rabbit and artichokes. Orange.
- Snack: Seed bread with olive oil.
- Dinner: Cauliflower sauteed with bacon. Scrambled eggs with roasted mushrooms. Banana with yogurt.

Thursday

- Breakfast: Milk Olive bread with slices of tomato and virgin olive oil.
- Mid-morning: Apple compote.
- Food: Roasted red peppers with pine nuts. Grilled pork loin with mustard and rice sauce. Khaki.
- Snack: Tuna mini sandwich.
- Dinner: Vegetable cream with croutons. Fried fish. Tangerines

Friday

- Breakfast: Coffee with milk. Toast with chocolate spread.
- Mid-morning: Muesli with dried fruit.

- Food: Stewed beans. Tortilla with vegetables and peas (Campesina) with lettuce. Grapes.
- Snack: Milk. Homemade cake.
- Dinner: Sauteed Brussels sprouts with chopped almonds. Spinach, goat cheese and honey crepe with zucchini slices. Pear.

Saturday

- Breakfast: Integral cookies. Pineapple yogurt smoothie.
- Mid-morning: Appetizer: assorted montaditos.
- Food: Migas. Nice pickled with onion. Banana flambé with chocolate.
- Snack: Macedonia.
- Dinner: Two-color puree (potato and beet) gratin. Baked carrot chicken thighs. Orange.

Sunday

- Breakfast: Coffee with milk. Ensaimada
- Mid-morning: Appetizer: assorted nuts, dried fruits, and olives.
- Food: Vegetable cannelloni au gratin. Grilled duck breast with fig sauce. Orange with custard
- Snack: Apple rolled with cinnamon.

- Dinner: Fine noodle soup. Eggs stuffed with smoked salmon gratin with grated carrot. Fruit frozen yogurt.

CHAPTER SEVEN
Mediterranean breakfast recipes

- Scrambled eggs with truffles

Ingredients

- 100 g shrimp (peeled and cooked)
- 3 egg yolks
- 125 ml of milk
- 125 ml whipped cream
- Sea salt (from the mill)
- Pepper (white, from the mill)
- 1 tbsp truffle oil

Preparation

1. Whisk the milk, cream, egg yolk and truffle oil in a stainless steel bowl, stirring constantly with hot steam until the egg begins to freeze.
2. Roughly chop the prawns and stir into the truffle.
3. Season the truffle eggshell with freshly ground salt and pepper.

- Spaghettiomelett

Ingredients

- 5 eggs
- 150 g spaghetti
- 30 g parmesan (freshly grated)
- 30 g butter
- 1 pinch of nutmeg (grated)
- Sea salt
- Pepper

Preparation

1. Cook and strain the spaghetti according to the package as required.
2. Beat the eggs in a bowl. Stir in the parmesan and season with salt, pepper and a pinch of nutmeg.
3. Mix in cooked spaghetti and stir well.
4. Fry half of the butter in a pan and fry the pasta mixture in a golden heat without stirring.
5. Melt the remaining butter on top of the omelet. Turn the omelet over and fry the other side until crispy.
6. Portion and serve hot.

- Croque Monsieur

Ingredients

- 2 eggs
- 1 pinch paprika powder
- 1 pinch of chili pepper (or grated nutmeg)
- Oil (for baking)
- 8 slices of toasted bread
- 4 slices of Gryère cheese (alternatively Emmental cheese)
- 4 slices of ham (or 8 slices of bacon)
- 200 ml of milk

Preparation

1. For the Croque Monsieur, the top half of the toast with a slice of cheese and ham or 2 slices of bacon. Cover each with a slice of bread. Mix the eggs with milk, paprika powder, chili or nutmeg on a deep plate.
2. Pour oil into a pan about finger-high and heat. Briefly turn the filled toasts in the egg-milk on both sides and bake in the hot oil on both sides with the lowest possible heat and with the lid closed until the cheese has melted and the toasts are a nice golden yellow. Lift out and dab the Croque Monsieur well before serving.

- Crab choux

Ingredients

- 250 g crabs (small, in the shell)
- 250 g flour
- 1 tbsp butter
- 4 eggs
- salt
- Vegetable oil (for baking)
- Parsley (for sprinkling)

Preparation

1. Bring the crabs in a bit of saltwater to a boil, lift them out, let them cool down and peel. Squeeze about 200 ml of cooking water through a hair strainer and bring in a saucepan to boil. Remove the butter and flour and keep simmering, stirring constantly until the dough comes off the surface. Remove the pan from the hob and continue beating the dough until it has cooled a little. Then add one egg slowly at a time and beat vigorously again. Add crabs, and let the dough rest for 15 minutes at least. Heat oil in a large saucepan. Cut the little donuts out of the dough and bake them in hot oil, golden yellow. Lift out, drain on paper in the kitchen, and sprinkle with parsley to serve.

- Greek yogurt with honeycomb

Ingredients

- 500 g yogurt (Greek)
- 150 g honeycomb
- 4 pieces of figs (fresh)
- 2 tbsp pine nuts
- Cassis syrup (black currant syrup)

Preparation

1. Peel the figs cut them into wedges and mix them with the yogurt. Roast the pine nuts, chop them and also pour them into the yogurt. Arrange yogurt in a bowl and drizzle with a little honey and cassis syrup.

- Tramezzini with egg and anchovies

Ingredients

- 12 slices of tramezzini bread (soft, juicy white bread without rind)
- 6 eggs (hard-boiled and thinly sliced)
- 12 anchovy fillets (inlaid)
- 200 g mayonnaise (homemade if possible)

Preparation

1. Brush the bread slices generously with mayonnaise. The top half of the bread with half of the egg slices.

Place the drained anchovy fillets on top and top with the remaining egg slices. Put the remaining bread slices on top and cut diagonally into two triangles.

- Herb omelet

Ingredients

- 12 eggs
- 12 tbsp herbs (of your choice, washed, finely chopped)
- 6 tablespoons of butter
- 1 tablespoon of flour
- 1/8 l milk
- salt
- pepper
- 2 tbsp parmesan (or other hard cheese to taste)

Preparation

1. For the herbal omelet, first, melt the butter in a pan and gently braise the herbs on a low flame. Attention: The herbs must not brown at all!
2. In the meantime, stir the eggs with salt, pepper, parmesan, flour, and milk into a liquid pancake batter. Pour carefully over the herbs, stir well.

When a firm crust has formed on the underside, turn the dough and bake. (Add a little butter to taste, so that the other side also becomes crispy.)

3. Arrange and serve the herb omelet on plates.

Tip

1. The herbal omelet can be eaten hot, is cut into pie-like triangles but is also perfect as a small bite with wine. The herbal omelet is also ideal as a soup inlay! In this function - a little modified and cut into small strips - it has also made a career in Viennese cuisine as a "fried soup".

- Caprese Toast

Ingredients

- 1-2 paradises
- 2 pkg. Mozzarella
- 1 clove of garlic
- 4 slices of toast
- 1 tbsp pesto (basil)
- 1 tablespoon of olive oil
- Basil (fresh)
- salt
- Pepper (from the mill)

Preparation

1. For the Caprese toast, first, wash the parsnip and cut it into slices. Also, cut the mozzarella into slices. Peel garlic and chop finely.
2. Brush the toast slices with pesto and place the parsnip and mozzarella on top. Mix the garlic and olive oil and spread over them.
3. Bake the toasts with the grill function of the oven until the mozzarella melts.
4. Salt and pepper the Caprese toast before serving and garnish with fresh basil leaves.

- Italian rolls ("pane arabo")

Ingredients

- 500 g of flour
- 300 g water (lukewarm)
- 1 pkg. Of dry yeast
- 1 tsp salt (coated)
- 1 tsp sugar (coated)

Preparation

1. Mix the flour, yeast, salt, sugar, and water and knead well. It should be an elastic and not sticky dough. Knead in a little more flour if necessary.

Leave the dough covered until it has doubled (approx. 1 hour).

2. Divide the dough into 8 parts and roll them out with a rolling pin to round or oval rolls. Place the rolls on a baking sheet lined with baking paper and cover them with a clean kitchen towel and let them rise for another 30 minutes.

3. Preheat the oven to 250 ° C.

4. Bake the rolls for about 10-12 minutes. From the 8th minute, check again and again that the rolls are not too brown.

5. The rolls can still be served warm.

- Eggs alla Saltimbocca

Ingredients

- 4 eggs
- Pepper (black, freshly ground)
- 4 slices of Parma ham
- 8 sage leaves (large)
- 2 tablespoons of olive oil
- 4 toothpicks

Preparation

1. Bring water to a boil in a saucepan and boil the eggs for 6 to 7 minutes until they are soft to the touch. Let the eggs cool, remove the shell and cut in half lengthways. Pepper the cut surfaces.
2. Halve the length of the ham and wrap a strip around half an egg.
3. Wash the sage leaves, pat dry and attach each leaf to the ham with a toothpick.
4. Heat the oil in a pan and fry the wrapped eggs over moderate heat for about 5 minutes until the ham is crispy. Turn the eggs.
5. Place two egg halves on a plate and serve immediately.

- Oatmeal Seasoned with Vegetables

Instructions

- 4 cups of water
- 2 cups of "cut" oatmeal (quick-cooking steel-cut oats)
- 1 teaspoon Italian spices
- ½ teaspoon Herbamare or sea salt
- 1 teaspoon garlic powder

- 1 teaspoon onion powder
- ½ cup nutritional yeast
- ¼ teaspoon turmeric powder
- 1½ cup kale or tender spinach
- ½ cup sliced mushrooms
- ¼ cup grated carrots
- ½ cup small chopped peppers

Preparations

1. Boil the water in a saucepan.
2. Add the oatmeal and spices and lower the temperature.
3. Cook over low heat without lid for 5 to 7 minutes.
4. Add the vegetables.
5. Cover and set aside for 2 minutes.
6. Serve immediately.

- Millo and flaxseed pancakes

These delicious pancakes are fluffy and popular with adults and children! Everyone keeps coming back for more. The combination of almond milk and rice vinegar creates the buttery taste that people crave.

Instructions

- 3 cups oatmeal
- ½ cup of millet flour

- ½ cup ground flax seeds
- 1 teaspoon of sea salt
- 1½ teaspoon baking soda
- 2 teaspoons baking powder
- 4 cups vanilla almond milk
- 2 tablespoons rice vinegar
- 1 tablespoon maple honey or date paste
- 1 tablespoon pure vanilla extract
- 3 tablespoons unsweetened applesauce

Preparations

1. Mix the dry ingredients in a bowl.
2. In a different bowl, mix the liquid ingredients.
3. Pour the liquid ingredients over the dry ones and combine them well.
4. Process the mixture well in a blender until smooth and lump-free.
5. Heat a pan over medium-low heat.
6. Using a ladle, pour the desired amount of mixture into the pan.
7. Turn the pancake when bubbles appear on the top, and underneath it is firm for approximately 5 minutes.

- Millet and buckwheat muffins with black currants

Ingredient

- ½ cup (90 g) of millet
- ½ cup (80 g) of unroasted buckwheat groats
- 4 chopped figs
- ¾ cup (160 ml) oatmeal or rice milk
- 1 tablespoon applesauce
- 1 heaped tablespoon (40 g) peanut butter
- 1 large ripe banana
- 1 pinch of sea salt
- 2 heaped teaspoons of baking powder
- ¾ cup (100 g) blackcurrants, fresh or frozen

Preparations

1. Dip millet and buckwheat overnight (or all day) in separate containers. Wash and drain (a filter can be used).
2. Soak the chopped figs in ¾ cup (160 ml) of oat milk for at least 30 minutes.
3. Heat the oven to 300-350 ° F (177 ° C).
4. Put the ingredients, except baking powder and blackcurrants, in a blender and mix them until a homogeneous lump is formed without lumps. Do not worry; It is supposed to be quite liquid since millet inflates considerably.

5. Now mix the baking powder. Unplug the blender and finally combine (DON'T LIQUID) the currants with a spoon.
6. Divide the dough into 9 muffin pans and bake for 33 to 35 minutes, until golden brown.

Apple and pumpkin pie

Ingredient

- 1 spoon ground flax seeds + 2 ½ tablespoons water (flax egg)
- ½ cup all-purpose gluten-free flour (or oatmeal)
- 1 ½ cup quick-cooking oatmeal
- 1 tablespoon baking powder
- 1 teaspoon baking soda
- 2 tablespoons pumpkin pie spice
- 1 tablespoon cinnamon
- 4 medium granny smith apples
- ½ cup date pasta
- 1 cup pumpkin puree
- 1 teaspoon vanilla extract
- ¼ cup of water (optional)

Preparations

1. Preheat the oven to 350 degrees F.

2. Mix ground flaxseed (flax) seeds with water in a small bowl and set aside for 10 minutes.
3. Mix all dry ingredients in a large bowl.
4. Cut the apples into thin slices and place them in a container.
5. Add the pumpkin puree, vanilla extract, flaxseed with water, and date paste to apples and mix well.
6. merge the dry ingredients with the apples and mix well. Add water if the mixture seems to be too dry.
7. Place the mixture in an 8 x 11 (2 quarts) container suitable for baking and bake for 30-35 minutes.

- Pumpkin and oatmeal bars

Ingredient

- 3 cups thick oatmeal
- 1 cup seedless dates
- ½ cup of boiling water
- 2 teaspoons pumpkin pie spice
- 1 tablespoon ground flaxseed or chia seeds
- ¼ cup small sliced nuts (optional)
- ¼ cup of vegetable milk
- 1 cup mashed pumpkin

Preparations

1. Preheat the oven to 350 degrees Fahrenheit.
2. Cut the date into small pieces, put them in a bowl, and pour hot water. Rest for 10 minutes.
3. Add dry ingredients to the bowl and mix well.
4. Add dates to the dry ingredients along with water, pumpkins, and plant milk and mix well.
5. Cover the square bread with baking paper and push the mixture firmly into the bread.
6. Cook for 15-20 minutes.
7. Allow the mixture to cool completely in the container, then cut into 16 squares or 8 large bars.
8. Store in the refrigerator for up to 7 days.

- Blackberry and lemon muffins for tea

Ingredient

- 2 cups whole grain wheat flour for baking
- ½ cup of Sucanat (refined cane sugar)
- 1½ teaspoon baking powder
- 1 teaspoon grated lemon peel
- ½ cup natural soy yogurt
- 1 cup non-dairy milk
- 1 tablespoon lemon juice
- 2 egg substitutes (2 tablespoons ground flaxseed with 6 tablespoons water)

- 1 cup blackberries
- 2 tablespoons coconut with reduced-fat and sugar-free content (optional)

Preparation

1. Preheat to 350 ° F (177 ° C) in the oven.
2. Fill a paper-coated mold for 12 muffins (or use a non-stick skillet).
3. In a medium bowl, mix flour, sucanat sweetener, baking powder, and rubbed lemon peel.
4. In a separate bowl, mix soy yogurt, milk, lemon juice, and egg substitutes.
5. Pour into the dry mixture the wet mixture and stir until it is hot.
6. Carefully add blackberries.
7. In the prepared muffin pan, distribute the mixture evenly.
8. Sprinkle the coconut (optional) on top of the muffins.
9. Bake them for 45 minutes in the preheated oven or until one of them has a toothpick inserted in the middle. Until serving, let them cool slightly.

- Cocoa, banana, and whole-grain spelled flour muffins

Ingredient

- 2 large bananas (I use frozen bananas and then defrost them)
- 2 cups whole grain spelled flour
- 1 cup walnuts, chopped into large pieces
- ½ cup raw cocoa powder
- ¼ cup applesauce
- 1 cup almond milk
- ¼ cup maple syrup, 100% pure
- ½ teaspoon baking powder

Preparations

1. Preheat the oven to 300-350 ° F (177 ° C).
2. Line the muffin pan with baking paper.
3. Crush the bananas in a large bowl.
4. Add the almond milk, maple syrup, applesauce, and mix them.
5. Add whole-grain spelled flour, baking powder, and cocoa powder and mix them.
6. Add the chopped walnuts.
7. Pour the mixture into muffin pans.
8. Cook the muffins for about 25 minutes or until when a skewer is inserted, it is clean.

Ingredient

- 1 cup unsweetened applesauce
- ¼ to ½ cup of seedless dates
- 1 cup oat milk (you can use another non-dairy milk)
- Egg substitute (2 tablespoons of flaxseed mixed with 6 tablespoons of water)
- 1 tablespoon apple cider vinegar
- ½ cup unrefined sugar
- 1 teaspoon cinnamon
- 1 ½ cups oat flakes
- ½ cup raisins
- 1½ cup whole grain wheat flour
- ¾ teaspoon baking soda
- 1 teaspoon baking powder

Preparations

1. The oven should be preheated to 300-375 ° F (191 ° C).
2. Puree with 1/4 to 1/2 cup of seedless dates with 1 cup of applesauce (depending on the desired sweetness).
3. Mix the linseed with water in a large bowl. Applesauce, milk, sugar, raisins, and vinegar are

added; blend well. Add the oatmeal, stir and set aside until all is combined.

4. Place the flour, baking soda, and baking powder into a separate bowl. Apply it to the mixture of apple and oatmeal and whisk until all is combined.

5. Pour the mixture into a lightly oiled silicone muffin mold with a spoon. (If you're using a regular muffin pan, cupcake papers should be used).

6. Bake the muffins till they are ready for 20 to 25 minutes.

- Pear and hazelnut crostini

Ingredients

- 4-8 slices of spelled bread (or baguette)
- 3 pears (Good Helene)
- 2 tbsp hazelnuts (chopped)
- 200 g yogurt (Greek)
- 3 tbsp maple syrup
- lemon balm

Preparation

1. First, stir in the yogurt with 2 tablespoons of maple syrup. Wash, peel, core and cut the pears into thin slices.

2. Toast bread slices or fry them in a pan with olive oil.
3. Brush the bread with yogurt, top with the pear slices and sprinkle with the hazelnuts and lemon balm.
4. Drizzle the remaining maple syrup over the pear and hazelnut crostini and serve the crostini.

- Feta and olive pancakes with bird salad

Ingredients

For the salad:

- 1 cup (s) bird salad (washed and dried)
- 3 tbsp cashew nuts (roasted)
- Apple Cider Vinegar
- olive oil
- sea-salt
- Pepper (from the mill)

For the pancakes:

- 100 g milk
- 200 g yogurt (Greek)
- 1 tbsp baking powder
- 1 tsp soda
- 150 g flour (smooth)

- 3 eggs
- 3 tbsp olives (black, chopped)
- 2 sprig (s) of thyme (leaves plucked)
- 100 g feta (crumbled)
- sea-salt
- Pepper (from the mill)
- Olive oil (for frying)

Preparation

1. Stir the milk, butter, baking powder, baking soda, flour and eggs for the pancakes first with feta olive pancakes and bird salad. Remove the olives, feta and thyme and season with salt and pepper.
2. In a saucepan heat the olive oil and fry the pancake mixture in 3 to 4 portions (thaler should not be too large). Turn and bake for 1 minute once bubbles have formed.
3. Mix the bird salad and the cashew nuts, season with a little vinegar of apple cider, olive oil, sea salt and pepper.
4. Mount the pancakes into a tower and serve with bird salad on the feta olive pancakes.

Bruschetta with mozzarella

Ingredients

- 1/4 kg tomatoes (diced)
- 2 cloves of garlic (finely chopped)
- 1 pinch of salt
- some pepper
- 1 pinch paprika powder
- 1-2 mozzarella
- 1 handful of basil (chopped)
- some olive oil
- 1 loaf (s) of ciabatta (cut into slices approximately thumb-wide)
- some sugar

Preparation

1. For the bruschetta with mozzarella, fry the tomatoes and garlic in a hot pan with olive oil.
2. Season with salt, pepper, paprika powder, sugar, and basil and let it brew for another 5 minutes.
3. Place the hot bruschetta on the ciabatta, place the finely chopped mozzarella on top and let it melt and garnish with basil.

- Greek omelet

Ingredients

- 4 eggs
- 150 g feta
- 2 tablespoons of olive oil
- Oregano (dried)
- Chives (finely chopped)
- Basil leaves (fresh)

Preparation

1. For the Greek omelet, pat the feta cheese dry with kitchen paper and cut into small cubes or crumble.
2. Pour oil into the hot pan and add whisked eggs. Then sprinkle the chopped feta cheese evenly over it.
3. Slowly slow down on a low flame, sprinkle with dried oregano. Divide the omelet in half, fold it together and sprinkle with chives on the plates.
4. Decorate with fresh basil leaves. Serve with bread and salad. Be sure to have pepper and salt grinder at the table.

- Masabacha green lentil curry

Ingredients

- 3 tablespoons of extra virgin olive oil
- 1 small onion, finely diced
- 1 ½ teaspoon of chopped garlic
- ⅔ cup of green lentils, rinsed
- ⅔ cup of red lentils, rinsed
- 2 cups of low-sodium no-chicken or chicken broth
- 1-2 cups of water, divided
- 1 ½ teaspoon of curry powder
- 1 medium-sized carrot, roughly grated
- ¼ teaspoon of kosher salt
- ¼ teaspoon of ground pepper
- 1 cup of thinly sliced arugula
- 2 tablespoons of finely chopped red onion
- 1 jalapeño pepper, sliced
- ⅔ cup of tahini
- 1 ½ teaspoon of chopped garlic
- ½ cup of ice water
- ¼ cup of lemon juice
- ¼ teaspoon of kosher salt

Preparation

1. Heat oil over medium heat, in a medium saucepan. Add the onion and cook, stirring for 5 to 8 minutes, until tender and translucent. Add the garlic and cook for 1-3 minutes, stirring. Add lentils, broth, 1

cup water, and curry powder, green and red. After high heat brings to a boil. Reduce heat to cook for 15 minutes and keep a simmer.

2. Stir in carrot and cook, stirring occasionally and add 2 tablespoons of water at a time if appropriate, until the green lentils are tender and the red lentils have broken down, 20 to 25 minutes more. Put away from heat, and add salt and pepper to taste. Cover. Cover.

3. Meanwhile, to prepare tahini sauce: in a mini food processor, combine tahini and garlic. In a slow stream add ice water with the motor running. Process, about 1 minute, until the tahini is light and fluffy. Add lemon juice and salt; process for about 30 seconds, until smooth.

4. Divide the lentil mixture on each plate between 4 plates, and dollop 2 tablespoons of tahini sauce. Arugula, red onion, and jalapeño top the lentils. Serve with the additional tahini sauce, if you wish.

- Mushroom olive frittata

Ingredients

- 1 tablespoon of olive oil
- 1 cup of sliced fresh cremini mushrooms
- 2 cups of roughly chopped fresh Swiss chard or spinach
- 1 large shallot, cut into thin slices
- 4 eggs
- 2 proteins
- 2 teaspoons of sliced fresh rosemary or 1/2 teaspoon of dried rosemary, crushed
- ¼ teaspoon of ground black pepper
- ⅛ teaspoon of salt
- ¼ cup of thinly sliced kalamata olives
- ⅓ cup of grated parmesan

Preparation

1. Cover broiler with preheating. Heat the oil over medium heat in a broiler-proof medium-nonstick skillet. Add mushrooms to skillet; cook, stirring occasionally, for 3 minutes. Add shallot and Swiss chard. Cook, stirring occasionally, about 5 minutes or until mushrooms and chard are tender.

2. Alternatively, whisk the seeds, egg whites, rosemary, pepper and salt together in a medium bowl. Pour egg mixture into skillet over vegetables. Cook at medium heat. Run a spatula around the

bottom of the skillet as mixture sets, raising the mixture of eggs so that the uncooked part flows below. Continue cooking and edge lifting until the egg mixture is fully set, and the surface is only slightly moist.

3. Sprinkle with olives; cheese on top. Broil about 2 minutes or until the top is lightly browned and center is set. Let stand, before serving, for 5 minutes.

- Broccoli-cheddar quiche with a sweet potato crust

Ingredients

- 3 ¼ cups of sliced sweet potato (approx. 1 large)
- 1 large egg, lightly beaten
- 2 tablespoons of grated parmesan
- ¼ teaspoon of salt
- ⅛ teaspoon of pepper
- 2 cups of broccoli florets
- ¾ cup of grated cheddar cheese
- 3 tablespoons of chopped shallots
- 4 large eggs

- 1 tablespoon of sour cream
- 1 cup of low-fat milk
- ¼ teaspoon of salt
- ⅛ teaspoon of pepper

Preparation

1. Preheat oven to 400 degrees F to prepare the crust. Coat with cooking spray, a9-inch deep-dish pie pan. In a medium bowl, whisk together sweet potato, 1 egg, Parmesan, 1/4 teaspoon salt and 1/8 teaspoon pepper. Move the mixture to the prepared pan and press it evenly to the bottom of the pan and to the sides. Bake for about 25 minutes, until the crust is set and begin to brown around the edges.

2. Evenly scatter broccoli, cheddar and shallots over the crust to prepare to fill and bake a quiche. In a small bowl, whisk eggs and sour cream, until smooth. Whisk in milk, pepper and salt. Pour the egg mixture over the other ingredients for the filling. Reduce the Oven to 350 degrees F. Bake the quiche until the filling is in the center and start browning slightly, for 35 to 45 minutes. Until serving to allow to cool slightly.

- Zucchini and oatmeal muffins

Ingredient

- 1 tablespoon ground chia seeds
- 3 tablespoons of water
- 1 cup unsweetened almond milk
- 1 tablespoon lemon juice
- 1 teaspoon vanilla
- 1 cup gluten-free flour mix (for example, from the Trader Joe brand)
- ¾ cup gluten-free oatmeal (create yours by grinding oat flakes in the blender)
- ½ cup flaked gluten-free oatmeal
- ½ cup unprocessed or unrefined sugar (for example, Sucanat or turbinado)
- 2 teaspoons baking powder
- 1 teaspoon baking soda
- 1 teaspoon pumpkin pie spice
- ½ teaspoon of sea salt
- 1 ½ cups grated zucchini
- ½ cup raisins
- ½ cup walnuts, chopped

Preparations

1. Preheat the oven to 350 ° F (177 ° C)
2. Line a mold for 12 muffins with paper coverings.

3. In a small bowl, combine the ground chia seeds with water and let the mixture stand.
4. In a medium bowl, combine the almond milk with the lemon juice and let the mixture stand. Don't panic if it starts to set - you are supposed to!
5. Mix the flours, corn flakes, sugar, baking powder, baking soda, salt and pumpkin pie spice in a large bowl.
6. Add vanilla and chia seeds to the almond milk and lemon juice mixture and beat until everything is combined.
7. Add the wet ingredients to the dry ones and mix them until they are combined.
8. Add zucchini, raisins, and nuts. Let the dough rest for 5-10 minutes before filling the muffin pan.
9. Cook everyone from 21 to 23 minutes. Once the muffins have come out of the oven, wait 2-3 minutes before transferring them to the rack to cool them.

CHAPTER EIGHT
Mediterranean lunch recipes

- Garden fresh omelets

Ingredients

- 1 ⅓ cups of coarsely chopped tomatoes, drain
- 1 cup of roughly chopped, pitted cucumber
- Half a ripe avocado, halved, seeded, peeled and chopped
- ½ cup of roughly chopped red onion (1 medium)
- 1 clove of garlic, chopped
- Cut 2 tablespoons of fresh parsley
- 2 tablespoons of red wine vinegar
- 1 tablespoon of olive oil
- 2 eggs
- 1½ cups of chilled or frozen egg product, thawed
- ¼ cup of water
- 1 tablespoon of sliced fresh oregano or 1 teaspoon of dried oregano, crushed
- ¼ teaspoon of salt
- ¼ teaspoon of ground black pepper
- ⅛ teaspoon of crushed red pepper
- ¼ cup crumbled, reduced-fat feta cheese

Preparation

1. For salsa, stir tomatoes, cucumber, avocado, onion, garlic, parsley, vinegar and 1 teaspoon of oil together in a medium bowl.

2. Whisk the eggs, egg product, water, oregano, salt, black pepper together in a medium bowl and crush the red pepper. For each omelet, heat 1/2 teaspoon of the remaining oil over medium heat in an8-inch non-stick skillet. Skillet with 1/2 cup of the egg mixture. Stir the eggs with a spatula until the mixture looks like fried bits of an egg surrounded by liquid. Stop stirring, but continue to cook until you set the egg. 1/3 cup of salsa spoon over one side of the egg mixture fried. Remove omelet from skillet; fold overfilling. Repeat to make a total of four omelets.

3. Serve per omelet with one-fourth of the salsa leftover. Sprinkle on 1 tablespoon of feta cheese with each omelet.

- Mediterranean chicken panini

Ingredients

- Olive oil non-stick cooking spray

- 2 small skinless, boneless chicken breasts (approx. 8 ounces in total)
- ⅓ cup of dried tomatoes (not oil-packed)
- 3 tablespoons of boiling water
- ⅓ Drain the cup of roasted red pepper in a bottle
- 4 teaspoons of balsamic vinegar
- 1 teaspoon of sliced fresh oregano or 1/2 teaspoon of dried oregano, crushed
- 1 large clove of garlic, chopped
- ⅛ teaspoon of ground black pepper
- 4 mini squares of wholemeal bagel bread or multigrain ciabatta rolls, divided
- 1 small zucchini

Preparations

1. Coat an unheated panini grid gently, covered indoor electric grill, or large non-stick skillet with non-stick spray cooking. Preheat to medium heat or heat, as regulated by the manufacturer. Stir in the chicken. Close the lid and grill for 6 to 7 minutes when using griddle or grill, or until chicken is no longer pink. (When using a skillet, cook chicken for 10 to 12 minutes or until chicken is no longer pink, turn once.) Cool the chicken slightly; divide each piece of chicken in half horizontally and cut into 2-inch wide slices crosswise.

2. Combine dried tomatoes with boiling water in a small pot. Cover and let 5 minutes stand. Transfer undrained tomato mixture to a small food processor (if you have a larger food processor, you will occasionally have to stop and scrape the sides down). Attach roasted red sweet peppers, oregano, balsamic vinegar, big clove garlic, and ground black pepper. Cover and work smoothly before.

3. Place the dried tomato-pepper place over cut sides of squares of bagel bread. Place the chicken on the bread squares underneath. Cut very thin strips from the zucchini using a vegetable peeler. Layer slices of zucchini on top of the chicken. Place the tops of the square bagel on top of the zucchini, spread sides down. Click gently. Coat each sandwich lightly with nonstick cooking spray at the top and bottom.

4. Put sandwiches on board, grill, or skillet, if necessary attach in batches. Open the lid and grill for 2 to 3 minutes or until bread is toasted, if using griddle or grill. (If you use a skillet, place a heavy saucepan or skillet on top of the sandwiches. Cook for 1 to 2 minutes or until the bottoms are toasted. Carefully remove the saucepan or top skillet; it can be hot. Flip the sandwiches; cover with the saucepan or skillet again. Cook 1 to 2 minutes longer or until the bread is toasted.)

Ingredient

- 16 oz white whole mushrooms or "crimini."
- 3 crushed garlic cloves
- ¼ cup onion, minced
- ¼ cup white wine or vegetable stock
- 3 tablespoon low sodium soy sauce or tamari
- 3 cups sweet spinach
- ¼ cup white beans
- 2 tablespoons nutritional yeast
- ¼ red pepper, minced

Preparation

1. Preheat the oven to 375 degrees F.
2. Remove the stems from the mushrooms, leave the tops intact and chop the stems.
3. Sauté the onion, garlic, and mushroom stalks in a pan.
4. Add the wine and the soy sauce or tamari, continue cooking for 2-3 minutes, or until the vegetables soften a little.
5. Add the tender spinach and sauté for a minute.
6. move the vegetable mixture to a food processor.
7. Add beans and nutritional yeast and mix to combine.

8. Transfer to a bowl and mix the chopped red pepper.
9. Place the mushroom tops with the top side down in a baking dish.
10. Fill each mushroom top with the mixture.
11. Bake for 20-25 minutes.
12. Remove from oven and serve hot

Crispy Cauliflower Chips

Preparation

- Ahead of cauliflower, cut into florets
- ½ teaspoon garlic powder
- ½ teaspoon of seasoning for poultry or seasoning without salt (optional)
- ¾ cup of aquafaba
- 1 cup gluten-free bread crumbs

Preparation

1. Preheat the oven to 450 degrees F.
2. Put the cauliflower in a container and season with the garlic powder and the seasoning for birds (or without salt). Be sure to cover the cauliflower evenly.
3. Soak the cauliflower, a foil at once, in the aquafaba, and shake off the excess.

4. Cover with breadcrumbs and shake off excess.
5. Repeat with all cauliflower florets.
6. put the florets on a baking sheet lined with baking paper.
7. Bake for 15 minutes.
8. Turn the florets over to bake evenly.
9. Bake for another 15 minutes.
10. Serve immediately.

Baked potatoes without oil

Ingredient

- 4 medium yellow potatoes
- ½ teaspoon garlic powder
- sea salt and pepper to taste

preparations

1. Preheat the oven to 400 degrees F (218 degrees C).
2. Cut the potatoes into sticks similar to "fries" of approximately ½ "- ¾" thick.
3. Put the potatoes in a deep pot, cover with water, and boil for 5 minutes.
4. Drain well and pour it into a deep container.
5. Add the spices and cover the potatoes well with the seasoning.

6. Put the potatoes on a baking sheet covered with a silicone foil or baking paper.
7. Bake for 35-40 minutes or until cooked and crispy. Enjoy your meal!

- Red cranberry and kale pilaf

Ingredient

- 1 cup of brown rice
- 1 ¾ cups vegetable stock
- 1 small yellow onion, diced
- 12 ounces (340 grams) of kale (approximately 5 cups)
- 3 or 4 cloves garlic, minced
- ½ teaspoon red pepper flakes
- ½ cup dried cranberries
- ¼ cup chopped cashews or other nuts (optional)

Preparation

1. In a medium-sized pot or rice cooker, cook the rice in the broth according to package directions.
2. Sauté the onion for five minutes, or until it is transparent.

3. Add the kale (without stems and thickly chopped leaves) and cook for another five minutes, or until the kale is soft.
4. Add the garlic in flakes and red pepper and cook everything for another minute.
5. Add the cooked rice and continue sautéing for three minutes, or until the rice has completely warmed.
6. Remove the pan from the heat.
7. Add red cranberries and optional nuts, stir well.

- Sweet potato tropical casserole

Ingredient

- 4 cups diced sweet potatoes
- 1 cup diced mango
- 1 cup diced pineapple
- ½ teaspoon unsalted garlic and herb seasoning
- ½ cup pineapple and coconut juice

Process

1. Preheat oven to 350 degrees F.
2. Combine all ingredients in an 8 x 11 (2 qt) baking sheet.
3. Bake covered for 25 minutes.
4. Bake uncovered for 5 minutes and serve.

- Traditional stuffing

Ingredient

- ½ cup vegetable broth
- 1 spoon low sodium soy sauce or tamari
- 4 cups gluten-free or whole-wheat bread cubes
- ½ cup chopped onion
- 1 cup chopped celery
- 1 tablespoon nutritional yeast
- ½ teaspoon bird seasoning
- ½ teaspoon garlic powder
- ½ teaspoon dried parsley

Process

1. Preheat the oven to 350 F.
2. In a small bowl, mix the soil flax seeds with the water and set aside for 10 minutes.
3. In a big bowl, combine every dry ingredient.
4. Cut and place the apples in thin slices in a container.
5. Add the pumpkin puree, vanilla extract, water-based flaxseed, and apple date paste and blend well.

6. Combine the dry ingredients and blend well with the apples. If the mixture tends to be too dry, add water.
7. In an appropriate baking dish, put the mixture and bake for 30-35 minutes.

- Quinoa Pilaf Stuffing

Ingredient

- ½ teaspoon sage
- 1 teaspoon thyme
- 1 teaspoon rosemary
- ½ cup wild rice
- 1 ½ cups quinoa
- 1 cup brown rice or rice mix
- ½ cup freshly squeezed orange juice
- 2 ½ cups of vegetable stock
- ½ sea salt
- 1 cup grated carrots
- 1 cup pomegranate seeds (optional)
- 1 cup gooseberries (optional)

Process

1. Heat a pot over medium heat.
2. Add the spices to the pot and sauté for 30 seconds.

3. Add wild rice, quinoa, and brown rice and stir for 1 minute.
4. Add orange juice, vegetable broth, and sea salt, and stir well.
5. Bring to a boil, cover and reduce heat to medium-low and cook for 45 minutes.
6. Remove from heat, add carrots and fruit, and serve.

- Mashed sweet potato with cauliflower

Ingredient

- 1 head of cauliflower, without the core and cut into pieces
- 2 large sweet potatoes, peeled and cut into pieces of 1 inch (2.5 centimeters)
- ½ cup unsweetened vegetable milk
- 1 teaspoon garlic powder
- Salt and pepper to taste

Process

1. Steam the cauliflower and sweet potato in approximately 1-2 inches (2.5 - 5 centimeters) of water until soft. Alternatively, you can roast them on parchment paper in the oven at 400 ° F (204 ° C) for 20 to 30 minutes.

2. Add the soft vegetables to your food processor and process everything for one minute to dissolve the ingredients, or you can crush them by hand. Add the vegetable milk, garlic powder, salt, and pepper and continue processing until smooth.

- Brussels sprouts caramelized with blueberries.

Ingredient

- 8 chopped dates
- ½ cup of water
- 3 cups fresh Brussels sprouts, cut in half
- 1 cup fresh blueberries
- 1 tablespoon miso paste
- 1 cup low-sodium vegetable broth or water
- 1 organic red onion, chopped
- 1 tablespoon soy sauce
- ¼ cup of nuts such as almonds, Brazil nuts, several mixed, etc. (optional) Pepper to taste

Process

1. In a food processor, mix dates with ½ cup of water until a creamy texture is obtained. Set it aside for a moment.

2. In a saucepan over medium-high heat sauté the Brussels sprouts along with the onion, miso, blueberries and ½ cup of broth or water. Cook covered for 10 minutes or until lightly brown.
3. Stir frequently and add the rest of the additional liquid as necessary to prevent burning.
4. Cook the sprouts until they are caramelized by the edges.
5. Add the soy sauce, ground pepper, and date paste. Mix and match well.
6. Serve and garnish with nuts.

Mediterranean chicken with 4 kinds of cheese

Chicken breasts with tomato sauce with lemon peel and a variety of cheeses are served with screw noodles.

Ingredients

- 4 portions
- 4 halves boneless and skinless small breasts
- 1 can diced tomatoes
- 1/2 cup chopped black olives
- 1 tbsp grated lemon peel
- 1 cup five kinds of cheese finely, shredded, five cheese and blend

- In some supermarkets they all come in a bag

Steps

15 minutes

1. The breasts are fried in little oil for 7 minutes on each side, or until cooked.
2. Add the diced tomatoes, grated lemon peel and cook for 5 minutes.
3. This mixture is added to the chicken and it is taken to the fire for 2 minutes until everything has been well mixed, and finally the cheeses are put.
4. It is served with a screw paste and is also sprinkled with tomato sauce.

Mediterranean beef casserole

Ingredients

6 portions

- 900 gr aguayo steak (round steak palomilla) diced
- 2 tbsp Butter
- 1 can 340 grams of tomato paste
- 2/3 cup beef broth or red wine
- 1/2 cup sliced black olives

- 2 tbsp light brown light sugar
- 2 teeth chopped the garlic
- 1/4 cup red wine vinegar
- 2 leaves laurel
- 1/4 cup grapes
- 1 cdts ground cinnamon
- 1 cdts ground clove
- 3 cups hot steamed rice

process

50 minutes

- Preheat the oven to 375 F in a bowl, mix the steak, the melted butter settles in a baking dish.
- Mix in a bowl the tomato paste, the meat broth, the vinegar, add stirring the olives, sugar, garlic, pour over the steak. Turning it to spread it.
- Put the bay leaves on top of the meat mixture; distribute the raisins, cinnamon, cloves, cover with aluminum foil.
- Bake the casserole for 45 minutes, take out the bay leaves, discard them, arrange the cooked rice in a serving dish and on the rice, spread the meat and the sauce by spoonfuls.

Ingredients

4 portions

- 1 sliced eggplant
- 1 tbsp cheese
- 1 1/2 tbsp chia of
- 5 oz cream cheese
- 1/2 roasted pepper cut into brunoise
- 1cda post or fresh basil
- for in dressing:
- 1/2 tbsp white vinegar, olive oil to taste a touch of pesto
- salt and pepper to taste (the ingredients are mixed and olive oil is added in the form of thread until emulsified)

process

30 minutes

- The eggplant is cut into thin slices and grilled until softened.
- Mix the cheese, pepper, and basil, Parmesan cheese with mayonnaise mix everything, wrap this mixture

with the eggplant slices and then add the dressing on top.

- Note: eggplants are put a decorative stick to hold. If you want you can take them to the oven but it is optional.

Mediterranean fish fillet

Ingredients

2 portions

- 2 steaks fish (Huauchinango, Robalo, Snapper, sea bream, etc.)
- 1-2 tomatoes
- 1 can mashed tomato
- black olives needed
- 1-2 teeth Garlic
- parsley
- Salt
- Pepper
- 1 Pope
- olive oil

process

30 minutes

- In a saucepan, we put olive oil and a clove of garlic chopped to brown when the aroma releases, add one or two peeled and chopped tomatoes, then add tomato puree, season with salt and pepper and add a peeled and diced potato 1 cm., we add some olives and chopped parsley. When the potatoes have been cooked, carefully place the fish fillets that are cooked over low heat, if necessary add a little water.
- Serve them with white rice.

Baked fish Mediterranean style

Ingredients

- 1 steak fish per person
- 3 chambray onions
- 1 tooth garlic for each steak
- red onion or échalots
- Salt
- Pepper
- dill powder
- olive oil
- Butter

- capers (optional)
- two lemons

process

20 minutes

- In a refractory we place our fish fillets on a little olive oil, and we put them on top: each: salt and pepper, a clove of minced garlic, chopped red onion or eschalots, the tails of about 3 small onions of chopped chambray and the onions are cut in half and placed on the sides, dill powder, a few capers, the juice of a lemon, olive oil and a piece of butter on top of each.
- It is put in a hot oven and you have to be on the lookout because it should not be more than 8 or 10 minutes so that it does not dry out, when we take it out we decorate the fillets with lemon slices.

Beef Meatballs in Vegetable Bath

Ingredients

6 portions

- 1/2 Bell pepper
- 1/2 stem celery

- 3 teeth natural garlic
- 3 teeth roasted garlic
- Chicken broth to liquefy the seasonings
- 4 ripe tomatoes
- 1 tbsp Mediterranean oil (canola-grape seeds-Extra virgin olive) to saute the seasoning
- 14 Large beef meatballs (baseball ball size)
- 16 oz of tomatoes in pieces with their juice
- 1 pinch ground turmeric
- 1 pinch ground cumin
- 1 tsp ground onion
- 16 ounces cooked and drained chickpeas
- Chicken broth as required.
- 1 cup carrots on thick wheels
- 6 pieces 1 baseball-size potato
- 1 cup peeled and chunky Aoyama

process

70 minutes

- Process the seasoning (the first 6 ingredients) and the tomatoes, in the blender covering with liquid chicken broth.
- In the pot you will prepare the broth, pour the oil and saute the liquefied seasoning.

- Add the meatballs, use pre-cooked and frozen. This speeds up the preparation process. Continue to soften and unite.
- Then add the carrot, chicken broth (I used broth prepared at home) but you can use the one you like. Add water to get the desired consistency. The Aoyama in pieces. Potatoes in large pieces. The can of tomato and the chickpeas drained.
- Add the Curcuma and cumin, after tasting taste.
- Reduce heat and cook until vegetables are tender.
- When extinguishing the fire add a sprig of thyme and oregano, preferably natural. Cover and let stand for 10 minutes before serving.
- It depends on the meat and personal taste, the fat is removed using a fat separator or allowing cooling because the fat floats on top and so you remove it.
- Accompany with white rice or bread

- Burritos of Cabbage

Ingredients

- One green or Chinese cabbage (12 leaves)
- 300 g ground beef

- One outing
- One clove of garlic
- 400 ml diced tomatoes
- One tablespoon tomato puree
- One tablespoon of taco herbs
- One small can of corn
- Two hands of grated cheese
- 100 gr kidney beans from a sack

Preparation

1. Chop the onion and then garlic and fry in a pan. Add the minced meat and then the taco herbs. Bake this loose. Stir in the tomato puree and cubes and then the drained corn and kidney beans. Let this burrito filling simmer for a few minutes. Meanwhile, boil water.

2. Heat the oven to 180 degrees. Cut the cabbage leaves and boil them (per 2 or 3) for a minute or 2 in the pan and then drain well. Place two cabbage leaves next to each other so that they overlap slightly. Spoon some of the burrito filling on one side, sprinkle with a little cheese and then carefully roll-up. Don't push too hard. Repeat this with the rest of the cabbage leaves and filling. If they are all in the baking dish, sprinkle them with some extra

cheese. Put the baking dish in the oven for about 15 minutes. Serve the carbohydrates with some rice (if the dish is no longer low in carbohydrates).

- Black Bean and Quinoa Burgers

Ingredient

- 3 cups cooked black beans
- 1 cup cooked quinoa
- 1 cup flaked oatmeal
- 2 tablespoons ground flaxseed
- ½ cup barbecue sauce
- ½ teaspoon of liquid smoke or smoked paprika
- 1 teaspoon garlic powder
- ½ teaspoon onion powder

Additional barbecue sauce for hamburger

Preparations

1. Preheat the oven to 400F.
2. Partially pest the beans.
3. include the rest of the ingredients and mix well.
4. Shape the burgers with your hands compacting well.
5. Put the burgers on a baking sheet covered with baking paper.

6. Bake the hamburgers for 15 minutes.
7. Flip the burgers and cover with a layer of barbecue sauce.
8. Bake for 10-15 more minutes.

Roasted Cauliflower with Turmeric

Ingredient

- 1 large cauliflower
- 2 teaspoons finely grated fresh ginger
- 1 tablespoon tahini
- 1 tablespoon organic miso paste, non-GMO
- 3 tablespoons vegetable stock
- 3 prunes or dates, chopped
- ½ teaspoon of turmeric powder
- 2 tablespoons tamari
- Ground black pepper, to taste
- Black and white sesame seeds, to decorate
- Sliced green onion, to decorate (optional)

Preparation

1. Preheat the oven to 425 degrees F.
2. Cut the leaves and stem at the bottom of the head of the cauliflower, so that it is flat.

3. Click with a sharp blade so that the spices penetrate the cauliflower.
4. Remove the cauliflower from the oven and sprinkle the top with one of the green onions (optional), the tamari, a pinch of ground black pepper, and sesame seeds before serving.
5. Mix the ginger, tahini, miso paste, broth, prums or dates, and turmeric in a food processor.
6. Rub the paste over the cauliflower using your hands, ensuring that it is spread everywhere, even at the edges.
7. In the oven, roast the cauliflower for 45 minutes or until golden is soft and cool.

- Creamy mushroom lasagna, gluten-free

Ingredient

- 3 cloves garlic, ground
- 16 ounces of chopped champignons (you can use a mixture of different champignons)
- 1 tablespoon of tamari or aminos (amino acids in liquid, in Spanish) of coconut or soy sauce, gluten-free
- 1 teaspoon dried thyme

- Thirty-four cup raw cashews, soaked for a few hours, drained overnight.
- 1 cup vegetable broth + a little more to saute garlic and mushrooms
- 2 large handfuls of spinach
- 10 ounces of lasagna sheets, gluten-free (I love Tinkyada brown rice pasta)
- 4 cups marinara sauce, purchased at the store (a 32 oz or 946 ml bottle) or homemade
- Nutritional Yeast (optional)

Preparations

1. In a skillet, heat a little vegetable stock at medium temperature. When it is hot, add the garlic and skip it until it releases the aroma. This will take a minute. Add the mushrooms, tamari (or coconut or soy amino sauce, gluten-free), and thyme. Cook, mix more or less every minute, for six or eight minutes or until the mushrooms release their water, and a small broth begins to form.
2. Combine cashews and vegetable broth in a high-speed blender and blend until the mixture is completely uniform. This may take five minutes, depending on your blender's speed and power. Verse the cashew sauce with the mushrooms in the pan. Reduce heat to medium-low and simmer to let the sauce thicken, stirring frequently.

3. make the lasagna sheets according to the package instructions. Be sure to do this after your mushroom sauce is ready so that the slices do not remain static for a long time and begin to stick. Spread a third of the marinara sauce in the bottom of a baking sheet eight to eleven inches in size (20 to 28 cm). Add a layer of sheets. Cover them with half the mushroom cream. Add a layer of sheets. Use another third of the marinara sauce to cover them. Add the remaining mushroom cream. Add the last layer of sheets and cover them with the remaining marinara sauce.

4. Cover the lasagna with foil and bake for 30 minutes. Remove the paper, add some nutritional yeast on top, if you want, and cook it for another 15 minutes. Let the lasagna stand for five minutes before serving.

Traditional Greek salad

Ingredients

- 2 tomatoes
- Cucumber
- 3 small red onions
- A handful of green and black olives

- 25 dag feta
- 2-3 tablespoons of wine vinegar
- 6 tablespoons olive oil
- 2 tablespoons oregano
- Salt
- pepper

How to prepare the recipe:

1. Peel cucumbers and onions, wash tomatoes. Dice tomatoes and cucumbers, and onions into rings. Mix the vegetables . Cut the feta

into cubes, add to vegetables along with olives.

2. We prepare the sauce: mix the oil with wine vinegar, season with salt and pepper. We pour the salad. We sprinkle with oregano.

Tomato and feta salad

Ingredients

- 2 tablespoons of balsamic vinegar
- 1/ 2 teaspoons of chopped fresh basil or 1/2 teaspoon of dried basil
- 1/2 teaspoon of salt

- 1/2 cup of roughly chopped sweet onion
- 1 pound grape or cherry tomatoes, halved
- 2 tablespoons of olive oil
- 1/4 cup crumbled feta cheese

Directions

1   Mix vinegar, basil and salt in a large bowl. Add onion; throw to coat. Let it rest for 5 minutes. Add the tomatoes, oil and feta; throw to coat. Serve with a slotted spoon.

Colorful layered salad

Ingredients

- iceberg lettuce
- tomatoes
- ¾ cans of corn
- medium cucumbers
- yellow pepper
- 2-3 red onions
- chicken breasts (about 0.5 kg)
- seasoning for peas and chicken
- 2-3 pieces of bread
- seasoning for toasts

- Butter and oil for frying
- Herb sauce

How to prepare the recipe:

1. Cut the chicken into small pieces, sprinkle with gyros and chicken, the season in the fridge for 1-2 hours.
2. Layer the salad in layers. We tear the lettuce and put the dishes on the bottom. Cut the tomatoes into halves or slices. We drain the corn. Peel cucumbers and cut into halves or slices. Then cut the peppers into strips. Cut the red onions into quarters of the slices.
3. We heat oil and fry chicken.
4. Cut the bread into small cubes, warm up the butter in a pan and pour the sliced bread on them. Fry until golden brown, sprinkle with a toast to the end of frying.
5. We prepare herbal sauce according to the recipe on the packaging and pour the whole salad before serving.

- Nopal Soup

What you will need

- 2 pounds of nopales, clean and diced
- 4 Roma tomatoes
- ¼ white onion
- 2 cloves of garlic
- 1 chipotle chili in adobo (optional)
- 3 cups of vegetable stock
- 1 tablespoon dried oregano
- Salt and pepper to taste

OPTIONAL COVERAGES

- Avocado
- Coriander
- Chives
- Lemon or Lime Juice

Preparation

1. Cook the nopales for 20-25 minutes in boiling water with salt or until they lose their bright color and are tender to bit.
2. Place the tomatoes, onion, garlic, and chipotle in a blender glass. Blend until you get a creamy consistency.
3. Remove the nopales from the heat, drain them, and rinse them with enough cold water. Leave aside.

4. In a pot, sauté the tomato sauce for about 3 minutes.
5. Add cooked nopales and oregano to tomato broth. Let cook another 15 minutes.
6. add salt and pepper to taste.
7. Serve on soup plates and add toppings.

- Matzo Ball Soup

What you will need

MATZO BALLS

- 1 ½ cups quinoa flakes
- 1 ½ cups of mixture gluten purpose flour
- 2 teaspoons onion powder
- 1 teaspoon garlic powder
- ¼ teaspoon of sea salt
- 2 cups of boiling water
- 6 tablespoons pumpkin puree

SOUP

- 1 medium yellow onion, chopped
- ¼ cup of Coconut Aminos
- ½ teaspoon freshly ground black pepper
- 5 medium carrots, peeled and sliced

- 3 celery stalks, diced
- 2 parsnips, peeled and sliced
- 1 cup fresh parsley, chopped
- 8 cups of vegetable broth without sodium

COVER

- 3 tablespoons fresh dill, finely chopped

Preparation

1. Preheat the oven to 200-300 degrees F (148 ° C). Cover a 15 x 13 inch (38 x 33 cm) baking sheet with parchment paper.
2. To make matzo balls: Beat quinoa flakes, flour, onion powder, garlic powder, and salt in a medium bowl. Add the boiling water and the pumpkin and stir to combine.
3. Take at least a tablespoon of the mixture and form a ball. Place the ball on the prepared baking sheet. Repeat until you have used the entire mixture. You should have approximately 30 balls.
4. Bake the matzo balls until they are a light golden color, approximately 20 minutes. Turn the balls halfway through cooking.
5. Transfer the baking sheet from the oven to a wire rack and let it stand for 10 minutes.

6. To make the soup: heat the onion in a large pot over medium heat and stir until it begins to release its aroma, approximately for a minute.
7. Add the Coconut Aminos, black pepper, carrots, celery, parsnips, and parsley and cook, stirring occasionally, until the vegetables release their aroma and are slightly soft, about two minutes. Add the broth and boil.
8. Reduce the heat intensity, cover the pot, and let simmer for about 35 minutes.
9. Serve immediately and place several matzo balls in each bowl of soup. Sprinkle dill in the soup.
10. The soup tastes even better the next day, and even better two days later.

CHAPTER NINE
Mediterranean dinner recipes

- Mediterranean Baked Cod Recipe with Lemon and Garlic

Ingredients

- 1.5-pound cod fillet pieces (4-6 pieces)
- 5 garlic cloves, peeled and minced
- 1/4 cup chopped fresh parsley leaves
- 5 tablespoons of fresh lemon juice
- 5 tablespoons of private extra virgin olive oil
- tablespoons of melted butter
- 1/3 cup all-purpose flour
- 1 teaspoon of coriander powder
- 3/4 teaspoons of Spanish sweet pepper
- 3/4 teaspoon ground cumin
- 3/4 teaspoons of salt
- 1/2 teaspoon black pepper

Preparation

1 Preheat the oven to 400 F.
2 In a shallow bowl, combine the lemon juice, olive oil and melted butter. Set aside Mix flour, spices, salt and

pepper for all uses in another shallow bowl. Put the mixture next to the lemon juice.

3   Dry fish fillet with pat. Dip the fish in a lemon juice mixture, then dip it in a flour mixture. Shake off excess flour.

4   Heat 2 tablespoons of olive oil over medium-high heat in a cast-iron skillet (look at the oil to make sure it is sizzling but not smoky). Add fish and sear on each side to give it some color, but don't cook completely (about a few minutes on each side) Remove from heat.

5   Attach the minced garlic to the remaining lemon juice mixture and blend. Drizzle the fish fillets all over.

6   Bake until it starts to flake easily with a fork in the heated oven (10 minutes should be finished, but start checking earlier). Remove the chopped parsley from heat and sprinkle with it.

7   Serving suggestions: Serve with Lebanese rice and this Mediterranean chickpea salad or the popular Greek immediately

- Chicken Shawarma

Ingredients

- 3/4 tablespoons ground cumin
- 3/4 tablespoons of turmeric powder

- 3/4 tablespoons of coriander powder
- 3/4 tablespoons of garlic powder
- 3/4 tablespoons of paprika
- 1/2 teaspoon of ground cloves
- 1/2 teaspoon cayenne pepper, more if you prefer
- salt
- boneless and skinless chicken legs
- 1 large onion, thinly sliced
- 1 large lemon, juice of
- 1/3 cup private extra virgin olive oil reserve
- 6 pita pockets
- Tahini sauce or Greek tzatziki sauce
- rocket salad
- ingredients of Mediterranean salad
- Pickled olives or Kalamata (optional)

Preparation

1 Mix the cumin, turmeric, coriander, garlic powder, sweet paprika and cloves together in a small bowl. Place the shawarma spice blend aside for now.

2 Pat the chicken thighs on both sides, dry and season with salt, then slice thinly into small pieces of bite-size.

3 Place the chicken inside a big bowl. Remove the spices of shwarma, and toss to coat. Add the onions, the juice of the lemon and the butter. Again throw all together. Cover and cool for 3 hours or overnight (if you have no time, you can cut or miss the marinating time)

4   Preheat the oven to 425 degrees F when they are ready. Take out the chicken from the fridge and let it sit for a few minutes at room temperature.

5   Spread the marinated chicken over a large, lightly oiled baking sheet pan with the onions in one layer. Roast the 425 degrees F heated-oven for 30 minutes. Moves the pan to the top rack and broil very quickly (watch carefully) for a more browned, crispier chicken. Remove from the frying pan.

6   Prepare the pita pockets whilst the chicken roasts. Create tahini sauce as per this recipe, or Tzatziki sauce as per this recipe. Create the Mediterranean salad3-ingredient according to this recipe. Deposit aside.

7   Open the pita pockets, to eat. Spread a little tahini or tzatziki sauce, add chicken shawarma, arugula, Mediterranean salad and, if you like, pickles or olives. Eat straight away!

- Moroccan vegetable tagine recipe

Ingredients

- 1/4 cup of Riserva extra virgin olive oil, more for later
- medium yellow onions, peeled and chopped
- 8-10 cloves of garlic, peeled and chopped

- large carrots, peeled and chopped
- 2 large red potatoes, peeled and diced
- 1 large sweet potato, peeled and diced
- sale
- 1 tablespoon of a mixture of Harissa species
- 1 tablespoon of coriander powder
- 1 teaspoon ground cinnamon
- 1/2 teaspoon turmeric powder
- 2 cups canned whole peeled tomatoes
- 1/2 cup chopped dried apricot
- 1 liter of low sodium vegetable broth (or broth of your choice)
- 2 days of cooked chickpeas
- 1 lime, juice of
- A handful of fresco parsley leaves

Preparation

1 Heat olive oil over medium heat in a large heavy bowl, or Dutch Oven, until shimmering. Add the onions, and heat up to medium-high. Saute for 5 minutes, tossing periodically.
2 Remove all the chopped veggies and the garlic. Season with herbs and salt. Toss to merge.
3 Cook on medium-high heat for 5 to 7 minutes, and mix frequently with a wooden spoon.
4 Garnish with onions, apricot and broth. Spice with a slight dash of salt once more.

5 Keep over medium-high heat, and cook for 10 minutes. Reduce heat, cover and simmer for another 20 to 25 minutes or tender before veggies.

6 Stir in chickpeas and cook over low heat for another 5 minutes.

7 Incorporate lemon juice, and fresh parsley. Seasoning to taste and change, adding more salt or harissa spice mix to your liking.

8 Move to bowls for serving and finish each with a generous drizzle of extra virgin olive oil from Private Reserve. Serve hot with couscous, or pasta, your favorite meal.

- Green salad with Chicken Rey and egg

Ingredients

- 1/2 iceberg lettuce
- 2 carrots
- 2 hard-boiled eggs
- 1 chicken breast
- 1 tomato
- Mayonnaise
- olive oil
- Pepper

- Salt

Preparation

- Wash and cut the iceberg lettuce to Juliana. We booked in a large bowl.
- We wash and cut the tomato into dice. We add to the bowl.
- Peel and cut the carrot julienne. We add to the bowl.
- Cut the chicken breast into strips.
- Cook the eggs for 10-15 minutes in a saucepan with a stream of vinegar and salt, so that they do not break.
- When the eggs are ready, we remove, cool with a jet of water and remove the shell.
- Chop the hard-boiled eggs into quarters and add to the bowl.
- Meanwhile in a pan with a drizzle of oil, place the chicken strips, season and brown the chicken for 5 minutes over medium heat.
- Mix the salad with a couple of tablespoons of mayonnaise to taste and serve immediately.

- Panera Bread Green Goddess Cobb Salad

Ingredients

Pickled onions:

- 1 cup of sliced red onion
- 1/2 cup white vinegar
- 1 tablespoon of sugar
- 1 1/2 teaspoon of salt
- 1 cup of warm water

Salad servers:

- 6 ounces of salad mix-use rocket, romaine, kale, and radicchio mix
- 6 ounces of grilled chicken breast
- 2 tablespoons of crispy cooked bacon
- 3 tablespoons of chopped avocado
- 1/2 cup of chopped tomatoes
- Halve 1 hard-boiled egg
- 2 tablespoons of feta
- 2 tablespoons of pickled onions

Green goddess salad dressing:

- 1 cup of mayonnaise
- 2 tablespoons of tarragon leaves
- 3 tablespoons of chopped chives
- 1 cup of flat-leaf parsley
- 1 cup of packed watercress cleaned and hard stems removed

- 2 tablespoons of lemon juice
- 1 tablespoon of champagne vinegar
- 1/2 teaspoon of salt
- 1/4 teaspoon of pepper

Direction

- Cut onions as thin as possible, I like to use the 1/8 inch setting on my mandolin. Put the onions in a jar wide. Mix white vinegar, sugar, salt and warm water in a small bowl. Stir until sugar and salt have dissolved. These should rest for about 30 minutes for use.
- Put all the ingredients for the dressing in the bowl of a blender or food processor and mix for 30-45 seconds, or until the dressing is mostly smooth and creamy.
- Place the salad on the bottom of a large salad bowl. Cut the chicken breast into thin slices and place on the salad. Add bacon, chopped avocado, chopped tomatoes, feta cheese, hard-boiled egg halves, and pickled onions. Drizzle with as much salad dressing as desired. Remaining salad dressing can be kept in an airtight container for 1 week.

- Caprese tomato, mozzarella, basil and avocado salad recipe

Ingredients

- 2 sliced avocados
- 2 ripe tomatoes
- 500 g mozzarella cheese
- 1 cup fresh basil leaves
- 1/4 cup olive oil
- 1/4 cup balsamic Aceto
- Salt and ground black pepper

Direction

- Gather all the ingredients to make this tomato, mozzarella, basil, and avocado Caprese salad.
- With a small knife, cut the end of the tomato stem and then, using a serrated knife, cut the tomatoes into slices.
- Cut the mozzarella into slices and see alternating slices of avocado, tomato, mozzarella and basil leaves in individual dishes.
- Sprinkle with olive oil and balsamic vinegar and season lightly with salt and ground black pepper.
- Spread your Italian tomato, mozzarella, basil and avocado salad with a fresh baguette or on a bed of romaine lettuce.

- Creamy Potato Salad

Ingredients

- 1 kilo of potatoes
- ¾ cups of low-fat sour cream
- ¼ cup of mayonnaise
- ¼ cup chopped fresh parsley
- 3 tablespoons lemon juice
- 2 tablespoons Dijon mustard
- 2 tablespoons chopped fresh tarragon
- 2 chopped celery stalks
- 2 hard-boiled eggs
- 1 small fennel, thinly sliced

Direction

- Peel the potatoes and cut them into medium cubes. Place them in a large pot with cold water and kosher salt to taste, and add a little salt. Bring to the fire and when it boils, simmer until the potatoes are tender 10 to 12 minutes.
- Mix mayonnaise with sour cream, mustard and lemon juice.
- Season with salt and ground black pepper and add warm potatoes. Mix and let cool to room temperature.

- Add the celery cut into thin slices as well as fennel and parsley and tarragon, all finely chopped.
- Mix so that the potatoes are impregnated with cream and add the hard-cut eggs in wedges. Serve the creamy potato salad.

- Wedge Salad with Creamy Dressing

Ingredients

- 1 cup Daisy Cream
- 1/2 cup skim milk
- 4 teaspoons cider vinegar
- 1 sachet of green onion powder mix
- 1 clove garlic, minced
- 1/2 cup sliced green onion
- 1 head of iceberg lettuce, removed the heart and in pictures
- 1 tomato, diced
- 4 teaspoons diced bacon

Instructions

- In a small bowl, combine the cream, buttermilk, vinegar and dressing mix. Beat until the mixture is smooth. Add garlic and 1/4 cup green onion; set aside. Remove the center of the lettuce and cut into 4 equal wedges. Place each wedge in four different dishes. Pour about 1/4 of the salad dressing over each wedge. Distribute 1/4 of the remaining onion, 1/4 of the chopped tomato and 1 teaspoon of diced bacon on top of each wedge.

- Tomatoes stuffed with tuna

Ingredients

- 2 cans of water or natural tuna
- 4 medium tomatoes
- 1 large cup of white or brown rice
- Mayonnaise c / n
- Green olives c / n
- Peas or capers c / n
- 2 carrots
- Salt c / n

Direction

- Place plenty of water in a pot and bring it to the fire. When it boils, pour the rice. Stir with a wooden spoon so that it does not stick and cook for 20 minutes or until it is soft. Remove, drain immediately and reserve in the fridge.

- Peel the carrots and cut them into small cubes. Cook in a pot with water until they soften. Drain and place in a bowl.
- Add the rice, the two cans of drained tuna, the peas or capers (cooked) and the mayonnaise to taste.
- Mix everything very well and room to taste.
- Wash the tomatoes very well and smoke them with the help of a knife and a spoon.
- If you want to take advantage of what you have taken to the tomato, cut it into small cubes and mix it with the rice or reserve it for another recipe.
- Fill the tomatoes with the rice and the tuna. Garnish with some mayonnaise in the center and a green olive.

Seafood paella recipe

Ingredients

- 4 small lobster tails (6-12 ounces each)
- water
- tablespoons of extra virgin olive oil from the reserve
- 1 large yellow onion, chopped

- cups of Spanish rice or medium-grain rice, soaked in water for 15-20 minutes and then drained
- garlic cloves, minced
- 2 large pinches of Spanish saffron threads, dipped in 1/2 cup of water
- 1 teaspoon Spanish sweet pepper
- 1 teaspoon cayenne pepper
- 1/2 teaspoon of Aleppo pepper flakes
- salt
- 2 large Roma tomatoes, finely chopped
- ounces of green beans, cut
- 1 kilo of prawns or large prawns or your choice, peeled and gutted
- 1/4 cup chopped fresh parsley

Preparation

1 Take about 3 cups of water in a large pot to a rolling boil. Attach the lobster tails and let boil until pink for a very brief time (1-2 minutes). Then turn off the heat. Attach a pair of tongs to the lobster tails. Do not waste cooking water on the lobster. When the lobster is sufficiently cool for handling, remove the shell and break it into large chunks.

2 Heat 3 tbsp of olive oil in a large deep pan, or cast-iron skillet. Turn the heat and add the chopped onions to medium-high. Saute the onions for 2 minutes then add the rice, and cook 3 minutes more, stirring frequently.

Now add cooking water for the chopped garlic and the lobster. Extract the saffron and the oil, paprika, cayenne pepper, Aleppo pepper and salt are soaking. Attach the chopped tomato and green beans. Bring to a boil and let the liquid reduce slightly, then cover (with a lid or tightly with foil) and cook for 20 minutes at low heat.

3   Uncover and scatter the shrimp over the rice, gently pressing it into the water. Add some water, if necessary. Cover for another 10 minutes and cook until the shrimp turns pink. Finally add bits of fried lobster. Turn heat off when the lobster gets warmed up. Garnish with peregrinate.

4   Serve the delicious paella with your white wine of choice.

- Spaghetti and Meatballs

Ingredient

- 1½ cup of water
- ¾ cup of millet
- 1 small yellow onion, finely diced
- 4 cloves garlic, ground
- 1 tablespoon dried basil

- 1 teaspoon ground fennel seeds
- 1 teaspoon red pepper crushed flakes (optional)
- ¼ cup dried tomatoes, finely chopped
- ¼ cup artichoke hearts, finely chopped
- ¼ cup roasted pine nuts or walnuts, chopped into large pieces
- 1 teaspoon sea salt (optional)
- 1 pound whole-grain cereal spaghetti
- 1 jar (28 ounces or 828 ml) hot spaghetti sauce
- Fresh chopped parsley, for decorat

Preparation

1 Preheat the oven to 375 ° F (191 ° C).
2 To make the meatballs, combine the water and millet in a small saucepan and bring the water to a boil at high temperature. Reduce it to medium-low and cook the millet until it is tender about 20 minutes. If it is not tender after all the water is absorbed, add two or three tablespoons of water and let it cook for another five minutes.
3 While the millet is cooking, sauté the onion in a large skillet at medium-high temperature until it becomes translucent and begins to brown, approximately for five minutes. Add the garlic, basil, fennel, and red pepper flakes (if you use it) and cook for another

minute. Add dried tomatoes, artichoke hearts, and nuts (if you use them) and remove the pan from the heat.

4   When the millet is ready, add it to the pan with the onion mixture, add the sea salt (if you use it) and mix well. Shape the mixture into balls using an ice cream spoon or a 1/3 cup measure and place them on nonstick baking paper.

5   Bake for like 15 minutes, turn them over and continue baking until the millet balls are lightly browned, about 15 minutes more.

6   To make the spaghetti while the meatballs are baking, cook the spaghetti according to the package instructions and drain it.

7   Transfer the cooked spaghetti to a larger tray. Top with meatballs and spaghetti sauce. Garnish with parsley and serve.

Oatmeal Seasoned with Vegetables

Ingredient

- 4 cups of water
- 2 cups of "cut" oatmeal (quick-cooking steel-cut oats)
- 1 teaspoon Italian spices

- ½ teaspoon Herbamare or sea salt
- 1 teaspoon garlic powder
- 1 teaspoon onion powder
- ½ cup nutritional yeast
- ¼ teaspoon turmeric powder
- 1½ cup kale or tender spinach
- ½ cup sliced mushrooms
- ¼ cup grated carrots
- ½ cup small chopped peppers

Preparation

1. Boil the water in a saucepan.
2. Add the oatmeal and spices and lower the temperature.
3. Cook over low heat without lid for 5 to 7 minutes.
4. Add the vegetables.
5. Cover and set aside for 2 minutes.
6. Serve immediately.

Rice with Smoked Sausages and Beer

Ingredients

- 14 smoked beef sausage
- 3 1/2 cups raw rice
- 1/2 onion in small cubes

- 1/2 chili pepper in small cubes
- 1 tbsp crushed garlic
- 1 cube chicken soup
- 1/4 cup tomato sauce
- water to prepare rice
- 1 tbsp Mediterranean oil (olive-canola-grapeseed)

Preparation

1 You add the oil to the pot you use; personally I prefer the quick pot for your convenience. Heat over medium heat; add the onion, bell pepper, and garlic, sauté, joining well.

2 Add the sausages, continue sautéing until they have browned the tomato sauce, and continue joining.

3 Rub the beer stream and continue joining while you jump. And you allow the alcohol to evaporate,

4 The rice, mix well and sauté for about 1 minute.

5 Add enough water to prepare the rice; this will depend on the pot you are using.

6 try salt and cook like normal rice

CHAPTER TEN
Mediterranean dessert recipes

- Italian apple and olive oil cake

Ingredients

- large gala apples, peeled and chopped as finely as possible
- Orange juice for soaking apples
- cups of all-purpose flour
- 1/2 teaspoon ground cinnamon
- 1/2 teaspoon ground nutmeg
- 1 teaspoon of baking powder
- 1 teaspoon of baking powder
- 1 cup of sugar
- 1 cup of private extra virgin olive oil
- 2 large eggs
- 2/3 cup of golden raisins, immersed in hot water for 15 minutes and then draining well
- Icing sugar for dusting

Preparations

1   Oven preheats to 350 degrees F.

2   In a cup, place the sliced apples, and add the orange juice. Just enough juice to throw in the apples and clean them so they don't shine.

3   Sift the flour, cinnamon, nutmeg, baking powder and baking powder into a large bowl. Add the sugar and extra virgin olive oil to a blender bowl with whisk for now. Remove at low temperature for 2 minutes, until all is well mixed

4   Add the eggs one by one with the mixer on and stir for another 2 minutes, until the mixture volume increases (it should be denser but still fluid).

5   With the dry ingredients in the large bowl, indent in the center of the flour mixture. Pour the wet mixture into the well (mix of sugar and olive oil). Replace with a wooden spoon until all have blended properly. It will be a thick batter (let nothing be added to loosen this).

6   Let the raisins dry absolutely soak in the bowl. And rid the excess juice of the apples. Add the raisins and apples to the batter and stir until all is well mixed with a spoon. The dough is going to be quite dense again.

7   Layer a 9-inch parchment paper cake saucepan. In the pan put a thick batter and align the top with the wooden spoon back.

8   Bake for 45 minutes at 350 ° F, or until a toothpick or wooden skewer has been inserted.

9   Keep it in the pan to cool completely. Just raise the parchment when you're done to put the cake in a tub.

The powder was containing icing sugar. Alternatively heat up some dark honey (those with a sweeter tooth like this option) to serve.

Chocolate Panna Cotta

Ingredient

- Half a liter of special liquid cream to assemble
- 100 ml of milk
- 1 tablet of chocolate for desserts (black or milk, to your liking) of 100 gr
- A splash (25 ml) of Grand Marnier or an orange liqueur
- 100 gr of sugar (or something less, it depends on the sweetness of chocolate and your tastes)
- 6 sheets of neutral jelly or 1 sachet of powdered gelatin (10 gr)

Preparation

1   Melt the chocolate in a water bath or in the microwave at medium power for about 5 min. We hydrate the gelatin leaves in a little water (about 10-15 min are enough).

2   Mix the cream with the melted chocolate over the heat and add the sugar, milk, and liquor, beating well so that the sugar dissolves. We must avoid getting to boil and we must not stop stirring so that lumps do not form. We also incorporate the gelatin and continue stirring until it dissolves well.

3   We fill some molds with this cream and leave in the fridge a few hours until it sets. I usually use individual silicone molds because it is easier to unmold and I like this candy more individually.

Drunk chocolate cake with mousse and strawberries

Ingredient

- 3 cups all-purpose gluten-free flour
- ½ cup date or coconut sugar
- 2 teaspoons baking powder
- 1 teaspoon baking soda
- ½ teaspoon of sea salt
- 6 tablespoons cocoa powder
- 4 tablespoons ground flax seeds
- 4 teaspoons vanilla extract
- 4 tablespoons unsweetened applesauce
- 2 tablespoons apple cider vinegar

- 1 cup raisins
- 2 cups of cold water

COVERAGES

- 8 cups fresh or thawed strawberries
- 4 cups of chocolate mousse

Preparation

1 Preheat the oven to 350 degrees F.
2 In a large container, combine flour, sugar, baking powder, baking soda, cocoa powder, ground flaxseed (flax), and salt.
3 In a blender, mix the water and raisins well.
4 Pour the raisin water mixture into a separate bowl and combine it with the vinegar, vanilla, and applesauce.
5 Pour the wet ingredients over the dry ones and stir with a whisk until well mixed.
6 Pour the mixture into a round baking dish covered with baking paper.
7 Bake for 30 minutes.
8 Remove from the oven and wait for it to cool.
9 To assemble the drunk cake, start by spreading a layer of chocolate mousse at the bottom of a cake pie bowl, a round bowl, or a cup of personal size parfait.
10 Cover the mousse with a layer of strawberries.
11 Place a layer of cake. If you opt for a personal parfait, you can use a round cookie cutter to cut the cake.

12 Repeat steps 9-11 until you fill the bowl or cup.
13 The last layer should be chocolate and strawberry mousse.

- crunchy quinoa bars

Ingredients

- 4-ounce semi-sweet chocolate bars
- 1 cup of dry quinoa
- 1 tablespoon of PB2
- 1/2 teaspoon vanilla
- For the peanut butter dressing:
- spoons of water
- 1/2 tablespoons of PB2

Preparation

1 Heat a pan with a heavy bottom over medium to high heat. Let it warm up for a couple of minutes before adding some quinoa Add 1/4 cup quinoa at once (so you'll have four batches to pop). Let it rest on the bottom of the pot, turning occasionally, until you start hearing the crackling of light, then constantly shake it for about a minute, until the explosion has slightly subsided. Be sure to take it off before it turns brown (it can happen very fast). You don't want anything but

a toasted golden color Once all of your quinoa has sprouted, place it aside in a small bowl.

2   In a bowl, add the melted chocolate, quinoa, PB2 and vanilla-mix to thoroughly combine Line a baking sheet with parchment paper and spread your chocolate quinoa mixture on top: you do NOT have to scatter the mixture over the whole pan, or it will be too thin. Just the middle form a square shape. The thickness is up to you - but in a small bowl, I made mine about 1/2 inch thick, add the peanut butter drizzle together. Sprinkle it all over the top of the chocolate and quinoa, then use a knife to shake it gently Refrigerate for at least one hour before slicing (or until it's absolutely hard). When sliced, I keep mine in the fridge, but the counter still works!

- Apple and pumpkin pie

Ingredient

- 1 spoon ground flax seeds + 2 ½ tablespoons water (flax egg)
- ½ cup all-purpose gluten-free flour (or oatmeal)
- 1 ½ cup quick-cooking oatmeal
- 1 tablespoon baking powder
- 1 teaspoon baking soda

- 2 tablespoons pumpkin pie spice
- 1 tablespoon cinnamon
- 4 medium granny smith apples
- ½ cup date pasta
- 1 cup pumpkin puree
- 1 teaspoon vanilla extract
- ¼ cup of water (optional)

Preparations

1 Preheat the oven to 350 degrees F.
2 Mix ground flaxseed (flax) seeds with water in a small bowl and set aside for 10 minutes.
3 Mix all dry ingredients in a large bowl.
4 Cut the apples into thin slices and place them in a container.
5 Add the pumpkin puree, vanilla extract, flaxseed with water, and date paste to apples and mix well.
6 merge the dry ingredients with the apples and mix well. Add water if the mixture seems to be too dry.
7 Place the mixture in an 8 x 11 (2 quarts) container suitable for baking and bake for 30-35 minutes.

- Blueberry muffins

Recipe

Dough

- 28 g coconut flour
- 56 g butter (melted)
- 56 g of erythritol
- 3 eggs
- 5 tbsp whipped blueberries
- 1 tsp vanilla extract
- 1/2 tsp baking powder
- 1/4 tsp salt

Topping

- 113 g cream cheese (softened)
- 56 g butter (softened)
- 5 tbsp whipped blueberries
- 1 tbsp erythritis
- 1/2 tsp vanilla extract

Cooking

Dough

1 Combine butter, eggs, erythritol, and vanilla extract.
2 Add coconut flour, baking powder, and salt. Beat until smooth.
3 Add the blueberry mixture and mix thoroughly.
4 Pour the batter into the muffin pan.
5 Bake for 30 minutes at 200 degrees.
6 Remove from the oven and cool.

Ingredients

- 110 g soft unsalted butter
- 30 g soft cream cheese
- 3 tbsp melted coconut oil
- ½ cup almond flour
- ⅓ cup of powdered keto sweetener to your taste
- ¼ cup unsweetened cocoa powder
- 1 tsp vanilla essence
- ⅓ cups of crushed chocolate without sugar (minimum 80% cocoa)

Cooking

1 Put butter, cream cheese, and coconut oil in a bowl. Beat with a mixer until smooth.
2 Add almond flour, sweetener, cocoa powder and vanilla essence. Beat well until smooth.
3 Add chocolate and mix.
4 Cool the mixture for 1 hour or until solid.
5 Form balls the size of a tablespoon and place on a baking sheet with parchment.

6   Cool the balls for another 30 minutes before storing them in an airtight container in the refrigerator or freezer.

- chocolate Custard

Ingredients

- 310 ml unsweetened almond milk
- 310 ml oily whipped cream
- 6 egg yolks
- ⅓ cup stevia or erythritis
- 2 tsp vanilla essence
- 225 g sugar-free chocolate chips

Cooking

1   Add all ingredients except chocolate and whipped cream to the pan. Beat well.
2   Put on low heat and stir continuously for 15 minutes until the mixture thickens.
3   Add the chocolate and mix well until all the chocolate has melted and mixed. To simplify the process, use a blender.
4   Divide the mixture into 8 servings.
5   Refrigerate for at least 4 hours or better at night.

6   Before serving, add whipped cream on top and sprinkle with grated chocolate without sugar.

- Chocolate Cake Espresso

Recipe

- 1 cup shredded dark chocolate (minimum 80% cocoa)
- 1 1/2 tsp vanilla extract
- 1/4 tsp salt
- 1/2 cup erythritol, powdered stevia, or another keto sweetener
- 1/2 cup unsweetened cocoa powder
- 1 tbsp freshly brewed and chilled espresso
- 3 large eggs

Cooking

1   Preheat the oven to 190 degrees and grease a round baking dish with unsalted butter. Put parchment on top and sprinkle it with a non-stick spray.

2   Put the pieces of dark chocolate in the microwave and heat for 1 minute. Stir and microwave again until the chocolate melts and becomes homogeneous.

3   Add eggs and sweetener to a large bowl. Beat with a blender or mixer at high speed for 1-2 minutes until

light and foamy. Add cocoa powder and espresso, and beat until smooth.

4 Pour the batter into the pan. Smooth the top with a spatula. Bake for 18-20 minutes. Remove the cake from the oven and let it cool for 10 minutes.

5 Drag the knife along the edges of the cake to separate it from the mold. Put a large plate on the form upside down and quickly turn the cake on a plate. Remove and discard parchment paper.

6 Let the cake cool completely and refrigerate overnight. Garnish with berries if desired.

- Chocolate Orange Cupcake

Recipe

- 1 chopped orange
- 4 eggs, protein separated from yolks
- 1/2 cup low-carb sweetener
- 192 g almond flour
- 43 g unsweetened cocoa powder
- 1 tsp baking powder
- 1/2 tsp salt

Cooking

1. Put slices of orange in a pan and fill with water. Bring to a boil and cook for 1 hour. The orange should be soft enough to be pierced with a fork.
2. Pull out the orange and cool slightly.
3. Preheat the oven to 170 degrees.
4. Put slices of orange in a food processor and beat in mashed potatoes without lumps.
5. Add almond flour, cocoa powder, a low-carb sweetener, salt, baking powder, and egg yolks. Mix well.
6. Beat the egg whites until foam and carefully pour into the orange dough.
7. Place the dough in a greased cake pan.
8. Bake for 1 hour until cooked.

- Coconut Ice Cream with Berries

Recipe

- 476 g butter whipped cream
- 226 g coconut milk
- 100 g of erythritol
- 3 egg yolks
- 4.93 g vanilla extract
- 155 g berries
- 40 g sugar-free coconut flakes

- 29.57 g of vodka (optional)

Cooking

1   Heat cream and coconut milk in a saucepan over medium heat for about 3-5 minutes. Do not let the mixture boil!
2   While the cream is warming, beat the eggs, vanilla, and erythritol together.
3   Remove the cream from the heat and carefully pour it into the egg mixture. Beat until smooth.
4   Pour this mixture back into the pan over medium heat and beat for 5-10 minutes until the mixture begins to thicken slightly.
5   Remove from heat, add vodka and mix (if desired). Allow cooling.
6   Add the berries and coconut, then put the ice cream in an airtight container and place in the freezer. Take out the container every 30 minutes and mix the ice cream thoroughly. This may take about 4-5 hours.

- Cranberry Low Carb Cookies

Recipe

- 56 g coconut flour
- 60 g soft cream cheese
- 1 egg
- 113 g unsalted butter (soft)

- 113 g low carbohydrate erythritol
- 1 tsp vanilla extract
- 2 tsp cinnamon
- 1/2 tsp baking powder
- 1/2 tsp salt
- 110 g cranberries
- 43 g low sugar chocolate chips

Cooking

1   Preheat the oven to 180 degrees.
2   Combine butter, cream cheese, and erythritol.
3   Add vanilla extract and egg. Beat until smooth.
4   Add coconut flour, baking powder, cinnamon, and salt, and beat until smooth.
5   Add cranberries and chocolate chips.
6   With wet hands, grab a large ball the size of a walnut and place on a baking sheet with parchment paper.
7   Press the top of the ball with your hand or the back of the spoon to shape the cookies. Repeat the process (you should get about 15 pcs.).
8   Bake for 20 minutes until solid and golden.

Ingredient

DRY

- 1 cup (120 g) raw buckwheat flour
- 1 ¼ cup oatmeal (155 g) oatmeal
- 2 tablespoons poppy seeds
- 2 teaspoons cinnamon
- ½ teaspoon cardamom
- 2 teaspoons baking powder

Wet

- 10 chopped figs
- A little more than 1 cup (260 ml) of vegetable milk, without sugar
- 2 ripe bananas
- 2 heaped tablespoons unsweetened applesauce
- 2 tablespoons peanut butter
- 1 pinch of sea salt (optional)
- ½ cup (50 g) dark chocolate (at least 70% cocoa), chopped
- 24 fresh or frozen cherries

Preparation

1   Preheat the oven to 355 ° F (180 ° C).
2   Cut the figs and soak them in the vegetable milk for at least half an hour. If you soak them more, place them in the fridge.
3   While the figs are soaking, finely chop the chocolate and set aside. Combine all other dry ingredients in a bowl. Place the figs and milk in the blender. Add all remaining wet ingredients and mix until smooth.
4   Pour the wet mixture over the dry ingredients and mix well. Make sure there are no lumps. Now add the chopped chocolate.
5   Fill molds 12 muffins (I molds using silicone) with the mass and finally hits two cherries on each muffin.
6   Bake for 25 to 30 minutes. Let them cool a little before trying to remove them from the molds.

- Homemade granola

Ingredient

- 3 cups flaked oatmeal
- ¼ cup chopped raw nuts
- ¼ cup raw pecans, chopped
- ¼ cup raw almonds, chopped
- ½ cup pure maple syrup
- 2 teaspoons vanilla

- 2 teaspoons cinnamon
- 1 pinch of salt (optional)

Process

1 Preheat the oven to 250-300 ° F (149 ° C).
2 Put all ingredients in a bowl, mix well, and cover everything with maple syrup. Spread the mixture on a baking sheet or broiler pan.
3 Bake for 30-40 minutes with occasional stirring until the mixture turns brown. Move the top plate to the wire rack and let it cool completely. Refrigerate the granola in a sealed jar.

- Tofu cashew cheesecake dessert

Ingredient

For The Mass

- 1 cup soaked cashews
- 6 ounces (175 g) of soft tofu
- 1 tablespoon peanut butter
- 1 small banana
- A handful of grated coconut
- 1 pinch of sea salt
- 1 ounce (30 ml) of water

- 2 tablespoons raw cocoa powder (mix it in half the dough)

The Swirl

- 1 tablespoon peanut butter
- 1 teaspoon agave syrup

End Mix

- 3 tablespoons of raisins, dipped in rum
- 4 chopped figs

Preparation

1   Soak the raisins in rum (not mandatory). (Of course, discard rum from children's containers). Soak the cashews in water for 2 to 2.5 hours. Rinse and drain.
2   Enter the dough ingredients (except cocoa powder) in the blender. Mix them until a uniform dough forms.
3   Now, put half of the mixture in a bowl and add the cocoa powder to the remaining half in the blender.
4   Mix half of the raisins and chopped figs in the brown dough and the other half in the white dough.
5   Prepare the swirl by mixing peanut butter (at room temperature) and agave syrup.
6   Now, start compiling the containers. Put the brown and white dough in the bowls in turns. Add small balls of butter mixture everywhere.

7   When you reach the last layer, add about 5 peanut butter balls on top. Now, it's all about your creativity and artistic skills. Take a sushi stick and make some cute swirls on top of the dessert.

8   Place the desserts in the fridge for a few hours. Cover the containers with foil if you need to keep them longer.

- Christmas nut cake with ginger

Ingredient

MASS MIX

- ½ cup unroasted buckwheat
- ½ cup of millet
- ⅓ cup (80 ml) unsweetened oat milk
- 1 ripe banana
- 1 tablespoon peanut butter
- 1 pinch of sea salt
- ½ teaspoon of turmeric
- ½ to 1 teaspoon of gingerbread spices
- 2 tablespoons baking powder (add them at the end)

TO COMBINE WITH MIXED MASS

- ¼ cup chopped hazelnuts

- ¼ cup chopped almonds
- ¼ cup chopped walnuts
- ¼ cup dried apricots, chopped
- ¼ cup raisins dipped in rum
- 5 chopped figs
- ⅛ cup goji berries
- 2 tablespoons grated orange peel or sugary orange peel (use organic)
- ¼ cup 50g (1.8oz) dark chocolate, chopped

Process

- Soak millet and buckwheat overnight (or throughout the day) in water in separate containers. Clean and drain them (you can use a strainer).
- Soak the raisins in a mixture of rum and hot water (half and a half) overnight. You can discard the soaking liquid later, or you can replace it with some of the oat milk in the recipe.
- Chop everything that needs to be cut from the second table.
- Heat the oven to 350 ° F (177 ° C) and line a bread pan with baking paper.
- Place the ingredients in the mixed dough, except for the baking powder, in a blender, and mix them until a uniform dough forms. Do not worry; It is supposed to be quite liquid since millet inflates considerably.

- Now, add the baking powder.
- Finally, combine (DO NOT LIQUUS) chopped nuts, dried fruits, and chocolate.
- Pour the dough into a bread pan and bake for 40 to 45 minutes until your Christmas cake is golden brown.
- Let cool before cutting and serving. If you leave the mold on the counter, cover it with a clean dishcloth or foil (loosely) to keep the cake moist.

CHAPTER ELEVEN

Mediterranean snacks recipes

- Grilled scallop top in cherry salmorejo

Ingredients

- 12 scallops
- 650 gr mature tomatoes
- 350 gr Cherries (I had frozen)
- 200 g milled bread from the day before
- 150 ml extra virgin olive oil Salt to taste
- 1/2 tooth Garlic

Preparations

1. We are going to make this cherry salmorejo, replacing part of the tomatoes of the classic salmorejo recipe with cherries. It is preferable that you use dark, very ripe cherries that bring a lot of flavors and enough color to the salmorejo, so that

the change is noticed (I had a few frozen and boneless)

2. The first thing to do is chop the tomatoes and crush them. If we want to include cucumber in the recipe, we also add it by putting it in the blender glass. Then we will pass the result through a fine strainer, leaving it in a bowl, so it will not be necessary to remove the seeds or peel the tomatoes.

3. As for the cherries, we remove the peduncle and remove the seed with a sharp knife or with a boner. Once we have the pulp of cherries, we crush it and add it to the bowl. Add the sliced bread and let it moisten and soften.

4. Finally, we add the olive oil and optionally half a clove of garlic. Crush the whole and rectify salt.

Coconut snacks

Ingredient

- 1 cup pineapple juice
- 2 cups diced mango
- 2 ripe bananas, diced
- ½ vanilla branch

- 4 cups shredded coconut
- ¾ cup roasted grated coconut

Preparation

1. In a small pot, cook pineapple juice, mango, bananas, and vanilla over medium-low heat for 5 minutes.
2. Scrape the seeds of the vanilla branch in the pot and discard the branch; then cook them for two more minutes.
3. Put the ingredients that are in the pot and the 4 cups of grated coconut inside a food processor with an "S" shaped leaf and process them until you get a mixture without lumps, but firm.
4. Let the mixture cool for about 1 to 2 hours, then, using a small scoop for ice cream or a spoon, place a small amount in your hands and make a ball before rolling it over the toasted coconut.
5. Repeat the process until all your coconut snacks are rolled, I bet you can't eat just one!

Cucumber and kale open sandwich

Ingredient

- 2 slices of whole-grain bread, toasted

- 2 to 3 tablespoons of hummus prepared without tahini or oil
- 1 chopped green onion
- ¼ cup chopped fresh cilantro
- 2 medium kale leaves, chopped into small bite-sized pieces (about the size of coriander leaves)
- ½ small cucumber
- Mustard of your choice
- Lemon pepper (Mrs. Dash and Frontier brands have no salt)

Preparation

1. Spread hummus generously on toasted bread. Sprinkle the green onion, cilantro, and kale evenly over the hummus.
2. Slice the cucumber in 8 circles and spread each with a thin layer of mustard.
3. Place the cucumber slices, with the mustard down, on top of the coriander and kale layer and press down, if necessary, so that they remain in place.
4. Sprinkle the open sandwich generously with lemon pepper, cut it in half or quarters, if desired, and serve.

- Baked zucchini in cheese breading with aioli sauce

Recipe

Zucchini:

- 2 medium zucchini
- 2 eggs
- ⅓ cup grated parmesan
- 1 tbsp almond flour
- 1/4 tsp garlic powder
- 1 tsp dry parsley
- ½ tsp sea salt
- 1/4 tsp black pepper

Aioli sauce:

- 1/4 cup low-carb mayonnaise
- 1 clove of garlic
- 1 tsp fresh lemon juice
- 1/4 tsp black pepper
- A pinch of sea salt

Cooking

1. Preheat the oven to 204 degrees.
2. Cut the zucchini into strips.
3. Beat the eggs in a medium bowl.
4. In a separate bowl, mix grated parmesan, almond flour, garlic powder, dried parsley, sea salt, and black pepper.

5. Dip slices of zucchini in beaten eggs, and then in the cheese-almond mixture.
6. Place the coated slices on a wire rack placed on a baking sheet. Leave in the preheated oven for 20-25 minutes until they turn golden.
7. In a small bowl, mix all the ingredients for aioli.
8. Remove the zucchini from the oven and serve immediately.

- Stuffed Eggs with Cheese and Olives

Recipe

- 4 eggs
- 3 tbsp sour cream
- 1 tsp mustard
- 33.75 g black olives (finely chopped)
- 33.75 g blue cheese (crumbled)
- 1/4 tsp sea salt
- 1/8 tsp black pepper
- 1 tsp finely chopped dill, for garnish

Cooking

1. Put the eggs in a pot of cold water and bring to a boil. Cook for 10-12 minutes, and then clean them.

2. Hard-boiled eggs, cut in half lengthwise, remove the yolks in a bowl and soften them with a fork.
3. In the same bowl, add sour cream, mustard, sea salt and black pepper, and mix well until a creamy condition is obtained.
4. Add finely chopped olives and crumbled blue cheese.
5. Fill the egg whites with the prepared mixture using a pastry bag or bag / rolled parchment with a hole.
6. Arrange the boiled eggs on a plate, garnish with chopped dill and serve.

Apple "Halloween" lamps

What you will need

- 6 red apples
- 1 cup peanut butter
- 1 tablespoon date paste
- ½ teaspoon of pumpkin pie spice
- 1 cup of oil-free granola

Process

1   Preheat the oven to 300-350 ° F (177 ° C).
2   Cut the top of each apple.

3   Take out the inside with a spoon or a melon. Make sure the walls are thick.
4   Carefully carve the face of the flashlight to make eyes and mouth.
5   Melt peanut butter in a saucepan until smooth and smooth.
6   In a bowl, combine melted peanut butter with date paste and pumpkin spices.
7   Fill the apples with the peanut butter mixture and replace the apple tops.
8   Bake the apples on a baking sheet for 10 minutes.
9   Place the granola in the apples and bake for another 10 minutes.
10   Serve immediately.

- Mediterranean recipe of toasted chickpeas

Ingredients

- 15-ounce cans of chickpeas
- tablespoons of extra virgin olive oil
- teaspoons of red wine vinegar
- 2 teaspoons of fresh lemon juice

- 1 teaspoon kosher salt
- 1 teaspoon dried oregano
- 1/2 teaspoon garlic powder
- 1/2 teaspoon broken black pepper

Manual

1   Preheat the oven to 425 degrees and line a parchment paper baking sheet. Drain the chickpeas, rinse and dry thoroughly, then lay them in a layer on the baking sheet.
2   Roast for 10 minutes, then take out of the oven, turn the chickpeas with a spatula so that they bake evenly, and then roast for another 10 minutes.
3   Place the remaining ingredients in a large mixing bowl and whisk. Stir in the hot chickpeas and shake gently back and forth until completely covered.
4   Put the coated chickpeas back on the baking sheet and roast for another 10 minutes. Occasionally make sure that they do not overcook and burn. Let yourself cool down and enjoy it!

- Bean salad

Ingredients

- 1 pound 15 bean soup mix, dry bean mix

- 1 liter of grapes or cherry tomatoes, halved
- 1 cup of fresh or frozen corn
- 3/4 cup diced red pepper
- 1/2 cup diced red onion
- 1/2 cup chopped shallots
- 1/4 cup chopped parsley or cilantro
- 1/4 cup of olive oil
- spoons of balsamic vinegar
- tablespoons of rice vinegar
- 1 tbsp honey
- 1 tablespoon of Dijon mustard
- 1/2 teaspoon ground cumin
- salt and pepper

Instructions

1   The bean mix bag is opened and the seasoning pack discarded, if included. Soak and cook the beans as indicated on the box. Drain into a large bowl and put it in it.
2   While the beans cool, whisk the olive oil together in a small bowl, all tablespoons of vinegar, honey, mustard, cumin, 1 teaspoon salt and 1/2 teaspoon ground black pepper. Deposit aside.
3   Pour over the beans, all the chopped vegetables and herbs. Drizzle with the vinaigrette, then toss to cover well. Good taste, then salt and pepper if necessary. Cover and refrigerate until ready for serving.

- Spicy red lentil dip.

Ingredients

- 1 cup of collected and rinsed red lentils
- teaspoons of curry powder
- 1 teaspoon onion powder
- 1 teaspoon of sea salt
- 1/4 teaspoon black pepper
- 1/4 teaspoon turmeric
- 1/2 teaspoon of Garam Masala
- 1/2 teaspoon cumin
- Crackers to serve

Preparations

1 Put the red lentils and enough water in a saucepan to cover them 1 inch.
2 Bring to boil, then heat down to medium heat.
3 Let cook until soft, for 15-20 minutes.
4 If you still have water left, drain it.
5 Crush the lentils with a fork (they should be quite soft already).
6 Pour in the spices and whisk.
7 Warmly serve with crackers.

- Coconut Bars with Nuts

Recipe

- 60 g macadamia nuts
- 125 g almond oil
- 54.5 g coconut oil
- 6 tbsp unsweetened grated coconut
- 20 drops of stevia

Cooking

1 Grind macadamia nuts using a food processor or manually
2 Combine almond oil, coconut oil and grated coconut. Add macadamia nuts and stevia drops.
3 Thoroughly mix and pour the dough into a baking dish lined with parchment paper.
4 Refrigerate overnight, and then cut into pieces.

- Spinach Cheese Bread

Ingredients

- 225 g almond flour
- 2 tsp baking powder
- ½ tsp salt
- 100 g soft butter
- 85 g fresh spinach, chopped
- 1 clove garlic, finely chopped
- 1 tbsp chopped rosemary
- 2 large eggs
- 140 g grated cheddar cheese

Cooking

1. Preheat the oven to 200 degrees.
2. Put the almond flour, baking powder and salt in a large bowl. Mix well, then add oil and mix again.
3. Add the remaining ingredients (if you wish, you can leave a little cheddar for the top of the bread). Mix well.
4. Put the dough in a cast-iron skillet, greased with oil, and form a pancake with a thickness of about 3.5-4 cm.
5. Bake for 25-30 minutes; then leave the bread in the pan for 15 minutes to cool.

- Roasted Chickpeas

Ingredient

- 2 cans of 15 ounces (425 g) of chickpeas, rinsed and drained
- 1 teaspoon garlic powder
- 2 teaspoons chili powder
- ½ teaspoon of sea salt
- 2 tablespoons lemon juice

Process

1. Preheat the oven to 400 ° F (200 ° C). Line a baking sheet with parchment paper and set it aside.
2. Place the chickpeas in a one-gallon (liter) sealed plastic bag and add seasonings. Shake well until completely covered.
3. Spread spicy chickpeas evenly over the prepared baking sheet.
4. Bake for 45 to 55 minutes, stirring every 15 to 20 minutes so that the chickpeas cook evenly, until golden brown.
5. Serve hot or cold for a snack at any time.

- Almond butter toast with sweet potatoes and blueberries

Ingredient

- 1 sweet potato, sliced half a centimeter thick
- ¼ cup almond butter
- ½ cup blueberries

Preparation

1 Preheat the oven to 350-360 ° F (177 ° C).
2 Place the sweet potato slices on baking paper. Bake until soft, approximately 20 minutes. (You can also cook them in a toaster, but you would need to activate it at high temperature for three or four cycles).
3 Serve hot, coat with peanut butter and cranberries. Store any leftover sweet potato slices, without dressings, in an airtight container inside the refrigerator for a week. Reheat them in a toaster or in a toaster oven and cover them as instructed.

CONCLUSION

The Mediterranean diet is not exactly a diet, but a diet. In the Mediterranean diet there is no calorie count, no fasting and no elimination of whole food groups. The main idea is good balance and moderation. Balance your food intake well and emphasize those that can be consumed in abundance. Don't overdo it - prepare small portions and consume in moderation.

Everyone should think about how the Mediterranean diet can best be tailored to their lifestyle and personal taste. Focus your menu on the foods this diet contains and focus on the foods you like the most. Sweet treats are not excluded, but it is desirable that they are consumed less frequently and in smaller quantities.

Be physically active by aiming for at least 30 minutes a day or 150 minutes a week. Maintain a healthy weight. Drink alcohol in moderation and give up cigarettes.